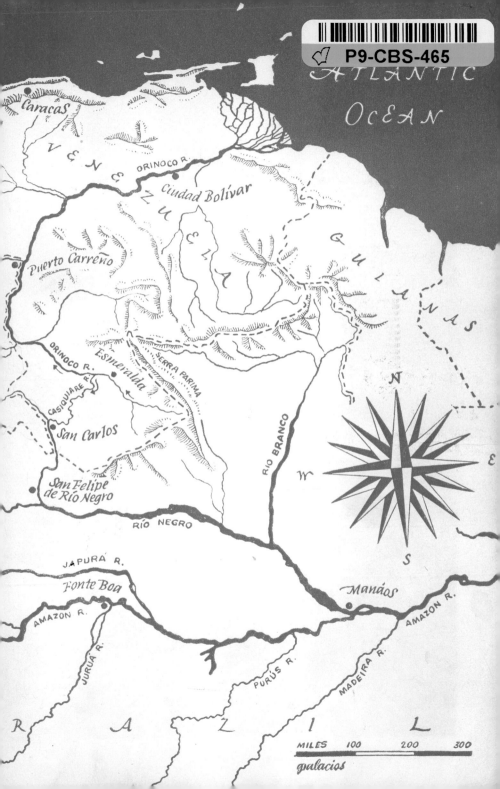

ATLANTIC
OCEAN

Caracas

VENEZUELA

ORINOCO R.

Ciudad Bolívar

GUIANAS

Puerto Carreño

ORINOCO R.

Esmeralda

SERRA PARIMA

CASIQUIARE R.

San Carlos

RIO BRANCO

N

W   E

San Felipe
de Río Negro

RÍO NEGRO

S

JAPURÁ R.

Fonte Boa

Manáos

AMAZON R.

AMAZON R.

JURUÁ R.

PURÚS R.

MADEIRA R.

B   R   A   Z   I   L

MILES   100   200   300

palacios

Orinoco Adventure

Orinoco Adventure

by Hector Acebes

ILLUSTRATED WITH PHOTOGRAPHS BY THE AUTHOR

DOUBLEDAY & COMPANY, INC., GARDEN CITY, NEW YORK, 1954

Library of Congress Catalog Card Number 54-5367

Copyright, 1954, by Hector R. Acebes
All Rights Reserved
Printed in the United States
At the Country Life Press, Garden City, N.Y.
First Edition

Designed by Diana Klemin

TO MY FATHER

An Explanation

In the summer of 1949 I met a New Yorker named Russell K. Crenshaw. I was on my way back home in Bogotá after a six months' expedition in Africa, and I had a monkey on my shoulder and was burned almost black by the sun. Crenshaw started talking to me on the plane, mainly, he later said, because he thought I was probably an entertaining lunatic.

By the time we landed in Bogotá we were close friends and have been ever since. One day Crenshaw suggested I put down some of the stories I'd told him; he said they would make a book. So I bought a portable typewriter, some paper, pencils, and erasers and went to work. That is how this book began, and I want to thank Crenshaw for suggesting it.

I also want to thank those who've helped me on one or another of the expeditions: Severo and Teolo Vargas of Ecuador; Pedro Pablo Díaz of the Vaupés; Señor Cayzedo, commissary of Mitú; Monseñor Gerardo Valencia of the Vaupés; Dr. Alfredo Camacho Ramírez, chief of Colombian National Territories; Fray Miguel de Huarte of Leticia; Dr. Julián de Zulueta; Dr. Richard H. Schultes of the U. S. Department of Agriculture; Roberto Londoño of San Felipe de Río Negro; Don Manuel Azavache, Cabo Perales, and Father Rufino Sánchez of San Carlos de Río Negro, Venezuela; the Reverend James Barker and the Reverend Eugene Higdem of the U. S. Missions in Venezuela; Excelentísima Señora Amalia Villacampa de Alfaro, Father Pedro Pablo Galindo, Burt Balaban, and dozens of other missionaries and civil and military authorities and friends in Colombia, Brazil, Ecuador, and Peru who have made my expeditions possible.

Those mentioned in these pages, some of them heroic, others villainous, are by no means typical of the countries in which they

7

live. The three million square miles of mainly unexplored jungle of South America make up a world that is without national borders, and its people are without nationality. Some may think I have been harsh on the Venezuelans in the account of the trip up the Orinoco. That is not my intention. I am certainly not judging that country by the handful of meddlers and opportunists I met up with on the river. There are people like them everywhere.

In three instances in the pages that follow I have changed the names of those involved. Catani is not named Catani. You will understand later why; although I have described our meetings without exaggeration, I feel I cannot reveal her actual identity. There are scores of people who know her, and I doubt if any of them will ever forget her. I know none of the men will.

Otherwise the adventures that follow are related exactly as they happened. I know because I was there.

H.R.A.

Illustrations

9

A typical trader's house on the Vaupés
A fish trap across the Abiyu River

Orinoco

The Orinoco River with Duida mountain in the far distance
The dance at Capihuara
The author
The heavily loaded boat on our way up the Orinoco River
Teolo digging for turtle eggs, Duida mountain in back
We make a stop to load up on turtle eggs
Duida mountain at Esmeralda
Getting ready for the departure after a night spent on the beach
The first Guaica Indian settles down next to Severo
A Guaica woman
A Guaica beauty
The lean-tos around the clearing of Mahakodo-Tedi
The official documents given to me by the Venezuelan authorities to carry out the expedition
Guaica bows

Colorados

A social gathering
A Colorado Indian

Leticia

The smallest Amazonian monkey

Llanos

Crossing Quebrada Honda in the Serranía de la Macarena
Getting ready for the day's journey across the llanos—La Macarena in background
Serranía de la Manacacias

Introduction

At thirteen I ran away from home; my plan was to sail all around the world, but I didn't get far. I was picked up at Barranquilla, Colombia's seaport on the Caribbean, and, when I got back to Bogotá, I still had most of the money I'd taken with me, the North American equivalent of a dollar.

At the time I was attending school in Colombia; so the next year my father sent me off to the New York Military Academy at Cornwall on the Hudson. I didn't run away from there, and I didn't talk much, either. One day at lunch I happened to mention that I'd shot a jaguar the summer before, which was true, but the captain of the table said I was a liar, and I didn't argue with him. At a military academy you don't argue much about anything.

That is one of the reasons, one of many, that I decided against becoming a professional soldier and was, during my three years in the U. S. Army, an eternal amateur. What's more, I never told the captain of my table that the jaguar is a highly overrated animal; like some people I've met, he looks dangerous and puts up an impressive front, but if you come across one and are unarmed, the best thing to do is shout, "Boo!" The jaguar will take off in the opposite direction.

You might say I've been running away from home ever since that first time. My first expedition took place when I was fifteen years old, and I've been on one almost every year since—barring those years when the U. S. Government provided me with a uniform and an all-expenses-paid tour to some of the less civilized sections of Germany, and the three years I spent at the Massachusetts Institute of Technology, from which I was graduated in June 1947.

I've still never talked much about my jungle adventures, though. At M.I.T. I usually confined myself to relating the unusual experiences I had had on week ends in generally unexplored parts of South Boston. Those were exciting enough. In the Army I kept my mouth shut. Privates first class in the Infantry are supposed to.

I expect I had better explain right here that I don't look like an explorer; what's more, my motives appear to be all wrong. The explorers whose adventures I've read usually have one foot on the carcass of an elephant or a lion or a tiger they've just downed, apparently with one shot. Their beards are invariably more luxurious than those I occasionally foster; their shirts are always open, displaying an impressive amount of chest hair. They are tall, muscular, and without exception broad-shouldered.

They always suffer a lot, too. They have been attacked by all manner of wild beasts of impressive size, not to mention snakes and rodents, and, sometimes, even a few large birds with mean dispositions. They have wrestled with alligators, always emerging victorious. They have subsisted for weeks on wild berries and raw fish. They have been attacked by bands of ferocious savages, usually of a cannibalistic nature.

Moreover, they never seem to have a good time. They went on their expeditions only in the interests of science or of mankind or both, and they can tell you if you will listen—and often if you won't—how many bones of what heretofore unknown animals they brought back for so-and-so museums. There must be lots of uncatalogued bones in museums.

As for me, in addition to confessing that I am only five feet, six inches tall, that my weight seldom gets above 135 pounds, that my shoulders are narrow, that the hair on my chest is sparse, I may as well tell you that there is no hope for future development.

When I was in high school I got up at six every morning for nine months and spent at least an hour working with dumbbells Charles Atlas was kind enough to sell me. I lost weight.

True, I have been bitten by mosquitoes and vampire bats and ants and a number of insects unknown to any naturalist, but I've also been bitten sitting on a screened porch in northern New Jersey. I have had a couple of mild brushes with an alligator, and once there was some doubt as to whether an anaconda or I would win an unscheduled wrestling match, but, generally, I have found that most jungle creatures are like the jaguar, as anxious to get away from me as I am from them.

In all of my travels I have never seen enough raw berries for a single square meal, let alone subsistence. Many of the fish in the jungle streams are edible, but only when cooked, and, although there is nothing much better than, say, broiled tapir, or turtle eggs, well cooked, I would dislike having to get along without the combined grocery-delicatessen I take along each time.

As for those explorers who like to refer to natives as "savages," wherever I've been I've treated the natives with kindness and respected their dignity. They have almost always responded in the same way. I have left hundreds of dollars' worth of equipment beside a riverbank and come back weeks later to find it intact, unless, that is, the natives had had some contact with civilization. In that case it is often gone.

Finally, let me make it clear that I have gone on all of my expeditions only to enjoy myself. I would rather be tramping through the jungle or going down a river in a dugout than sitting at a desk figuring out next year's income tax. If I weren't married and didn't have two daughters and a son to support, I expect I would never come back. There have been months when I haven't read a single newspaper or listened to a news broadcast, and on my return I have invariably discovered that the world was in just about the same sad shape as when I left.

Another thing, I notice a lot of explorers never seem to be frightened. I often am.

Once in Africa on an elephant hunt I took to the nearest tree when a herd thundered by.

My guide, a man who liked to refer to himself as fearless and who may have been, shouted up at me angrily when the elephants had disappeared.

"What the hell are you," he wanted to know, "a man or a mouse?"

"Right now," I shouted back, "I'm a mouse."

When, as so rarely happens, people ask me why I am taking off for the unknown, I simply say, "Because it's fun."

There are many who do not approve of fun any more, but, fortunately, they are not in the majority.

What follows is for those who do.

Hector R. Acebes

Orinoco Adventure

1

Villavicencio was not a beautiful town when I first visited it fifteen years ago, and it still isn't. Its cobblestone streets are wide and often unswept. In 1938 most of its houses were made of baked mud carelessly coated with whitewash. It had a permanent population of 10,000, including many Indians, an uncounted horde of itinerant prostitutes, and scores of wandering Colombian *llaneros*, or cowboys. There were hundreds of bars; drunkenness was frequent on week ends, and even the mildest argument was likely to end in a shooting or, at the very least, a knifing or two.

However, when I first arrived, Villavicencio seemed to me the most exciting village in all the world. I was alone, and I was beginning my first expedition. There have been many others since, all of them to more remote spots, most of them longer, many more dangerous, but to me the first will always be the best. For one thing, that was when I met Catani. For another, I was only fifteen.

To get there, I had come in a rickety ancient bus from my home in Bogotá. The driver was a swarthy, cheerful young man who was constantly surprised and delighted with the intricacies of his vehicle. I am fairly certain that he had never driven an automobile before and possibly never even ridden in one. The road was a single narrow lane cut into the side of the eastern Andes. One slip at any point along the route would have meant death for all of us, a fact that seemed to challenge the driver to a recklessness unusual even in Colombia, where safety almost always comes last. On the straightaways, which were infrequent, he slowed down to a crawl; on the narrow curves, he seemed to be rehearsing for the Indianapolis speedway. His skill was non-existent, but, when he had, by the grace of God, escaped going over the side, most of the passengers, the majority of whom were *llaneros*, laughed and cheered. When, for a few rare moments, he actually drove sensibly, they were morose and disappointed.

We had to stop along the way while heavy chains were raised from across the road. Traffic was one-way only, but when I asked the keeper of one of the chains what would happen if we met another vehicle in between one of the villages, he merely shrugged. Such a possibility, he said, had never occurred to him. His job was to raise and lower the chain; there were others whose business it was to think about the solutions to such intricate problems.

However, I didn't worry. I never do. How, someone is always asking me, can I be sure I won't be murdered in my sleep when I am among a tribe of uncivilized Indians? How can I be positive that I will not step on a poisonous snake as I trek through an unexplored jungle? The answer is that I can never be certain. If I were to worry about such possibilities, I ought to stay home, where, of course, I might break my neck by a fall in the bathtub. An adventurer ought to have a philosophical turn of mind; otherwise he would be happier as a bank teller.

Late in the afternoon, as the creaking bus lurched around an especially narrow curve, I looked below and gasped. Spread out in the valley was a never-ending sea of soft, pale yellow grass swaying gently in the breeze and dark green-blue patches of jungle. This was the *llanos*, the vast, still largely unexplored plains stretching all the way from the eastern Andes to the Venezuelan border.

As I watched, the sun emerged from behind a cloud, mixing gold with the varying greens and yellows, and, from out of the intermittent circles of jungle, clouds of vapor rose. It was as if scores of campfires had been started all at once. Even the usually

18

phlegmatic llaneros leaned out of the paneless windows and gazed below. Somewhere in the back of the bus a baby was crying, and near the front a hunchbacked, emaciated old llanero quietly strummed an antique guitar and sang a mournful song of the llanos.

"Above the plain, the palm,
 Above the palm, the sky,
 Above my horse, I;
 And above me, my hat."

I felt wonderful. A new life had begun. True, in two months I would be going to the New York Military Academy, where, my father was sure, some of what he called "this exploring foolishness" would be knocked out of me, but in the meantime I was on my own. I was about to explore the mysteries of the llanos, a region where, according to Colombian legend, many enter, but few return.

Right then I didn't care about returning. Perhaps in the llanos I would discover the long-lost El Dorado, where all the cities were built of gold; I might find a hitherto unknown Indian tribe; at the very least I would have some unforgettable adventures. I felt like a character out of Jules Verne or W. H. Hudson or Robert Louis Stevenson. I felt like Sir Henry Morton Stanley and David Livingstone. I felt like singing, and as the old man continued I hummed with him. The bus driver, who was already keeping time with one hand, turned around, threw back his head, and joined us. He sang much better than he drove.

The bus finally ground to an agonized stop in front of the village square, and as I unloaded my bags the rain began. In July it rains almost incessantly in Villavicencio. It rains for a while in the morning, for a while in the afternoon, and for a while at night, and some days and some nights it does not stop raining at all. The rain diminishes a little every day until January. It begins raining heavily again in late February.

The streets were crowded with llaneros, small men, their leathery skins permanently darkened by the sun and wind, their bodies thin and wiry, their legs inevitably bowed and scrawny, their eyes narrowed and crinkled. Over their shoulders many had draped *ruanas*, square pieces of dark wool with slits in the center to fit over their heads. On the trail the ruana serves as a topcoat, raincoat, and, on chilly nights, a blanket.

The llaneros usually wear wide leather belts slung low across their hips, often with a pistol attached. They have long spurs strapped to their ankles and almost always carry a machete. Their leather leggings are usually knee length; their trousers tight and frequently stained with sweat, cow dung, and less identifiable spots; their shirts are invariably patched, their sombreros uniformly battered.

They are always lonely men, grazing their herds on the llanos for months without seeing another human being, then leading them across the wide plains to Villavicencio, where they are fattened in the haciendas on the outskirts, and finally trucked or driven on foot to Bogotá, where they are sold.

Villavicencio was then one of the most drunken spots on earth. I was told that 10,000 bottles of beer were sold every day over the week end, an average of a bottle apiece for every man, woman, and child who lived there, plus rum and whiskey and *aguardiente*, a whitish drink with a wallop so strong I've seen whole villages in a stupor for days after an evening of celebration.

As I watched, two llaneros staggered down the street, arm in arm and singing. Further along two more were cursing and fighting; one had a long, businesslike knife, but nobody paid the slight-

20

est attention, including a weary policeman who watched phleg-
matically from across the street. Across the way four more llaneros
were wrestling drunkenly, and a fifth threw a whiskey bottle
against the side of a house; the glass shattered noisily, and the
man laughed. The bottle was empty.

Meantime the rain continued.

A few minutes later I checked in at the hotel, which was small,
ugly, and dirty. The bed was narrow and the mattress hard. There
were a few crooked nails on the wall for hanging clothes on, a
washbasin and a chipped pitcher half filled with brackish water, a
small bedpan painted a gay red and blue, and a single straight-
backed chair. I spent that night on the floor, which seemed to be
somewhat cleaner than the bed. The only trouble was the danger
of falling through the considerable space between each board.

I threw my bags on the floor, washed up, and went down to
dinner, which was delicious. The steak was rare and tender.

After dinner I walked into the narrow, airless lobby. There I
met Pedro. He was short and so thin I was sure he'd never really
had enough to eat; his complexion was sallow; his head almost
completely bald, and when he smiled he exhibited a few real
teeth, a large number of gold ones, and numerous gaps where
teeth had once been. He wore trousers that were more nearly
mottled brown and gray than white, a shirt with wide green
stripes, and what remained of a Panama hat. There are men like
Pedro in every city and town of the world.

He bowed. "I am," he said after introducing himself, "here to
aid you, Doctor Acebes." In Colombia "doctor" is used as a form
of flattery.

I said no, I didn't need any help, thanks.

Pedro, who had an expressive face, looked sad.

I was Hector R. Acebes of Bogotá, was I not? I nodded. I was

21

on my way across the llanos to Puerto Carreño, was I not? I nodded, but to this day I don't know how he found out. I hadn't spoken to anyone about my trip since leaving Bogotá. However, the Pedros of the world always know.

Well, said Pedro, bowing again; he knew where I could find the best *vaqueano* (plainsman) in all of Colombia; by coincidence he was going in my direction, and it might be that, with Pedro's help, I could persuade him to take me along. Would I be interested?

I grinned and shrugged. After all, it was Saturday night, and I wanted to leave on Monday morning. I had nothing to lose.

After a few steps Pedro explained that our destination was the red-light district, a few steps up this street and a few more down that one. He smiled broadly. There were, he said, many beautiful girls here. He pointed to a trio sitting under the sodden awning of a forlorn sidewalk café. All three were, he said, close friends of his. Now which would I prefer? The thin, dark Negro girl with her oiled hair piled high on her head? The fat one, perhaps, who appeared to be mainly Indian? Or the young one, who was of many strains and had soft eyes that were deep blue?

I thanked Pedro but shook my head. Well, he said, if I wanted to be foolish; if I wished to deny myself pleasure. His shoulders drooped as if I had insulted him.

Then he darted down a side street, beckoning me to follow. After a block or so he opened the door of one of the many dark cafés, and I went in after him. A juke box was blaring a boogie-woogie song; the bartender, a squat, exceedingly fat man, was moaning an obbligato. Near the door a svelte, brown girl haggled with a handsome young llanero. At one point the girl became angry, and the policeman who had been standing nearby grinned tolerantly and turned away. Obviously he wanted to stay out of trouble. Finally the llanero frowned and threw a handful of pesos on the floor near the girl. She spat at him, then knelt and picked up the bills.

As my eyes got used to the semidarkness and the thick haze of smoke, I saw that over the bar were two large paintings, one of a voluptuous blonde lying on her back, the other of an equally voluptuous brunette standing up and facing the artist. Both were completely nude.

At each of the dozens of tiny round tables sat one or two girls and an equal number of llaneros. The girls were of all sizes, shapes, and colors. However, most of them were young, some no more than thirteen or fourteen, others, bent and already haggard and old, may have been as much as twenty-five or -six. I imagine one crone who sat by herself in a corner was probably thirty. The climate and their vocation both work against longevity. Most of them wore sleazy imitation satin dresses, short and tight-fitting. They wore huge earrings and, on their arms, jangling bracelets. All of them were heavily painted.

On the top of each table were twenty, sometimes as many as thirty or forty empty bottles of beer plus a few that were half full but wouldn't be for long.

The air was filled with cigar and cigarette smoke, the odor of meals long since forgotten, and of bodies unused to baths. There were flies everywhere, on the bar, on the ceiling, on the floor, on the waiters and the customers.

Pedro turned toward me and grinned proudly. "Nice," he said, "very nice."

Then he led me to a table slightly larger than the others. Three young prostitutes were seated around it. None could have been more than sixteen, but they all had a hard, tired look.

They looked up at us and frowned. Between them were three

men, one middle-aged, with a weary smile, milky eyes in which the pupils seemed almost to have disappeared and a scarred face. The other two were good-looking young llaneros, whose names, I later learned, were Pablo and Luis.

The older man was Don Ramón, and, after Pedro had explained what I wanted, he grinned, displaying a few discolored stubs of teeth.

Yes, he said, tilting back a beer bottle and drinking half in a single swallow, he was going across the llanos as far as Orocue, a tiny village on the Meta River which is the only trading post for hundreds of square miles. If I was willing to pay my own expenses, Don Ramón said, he, Luis, and Pablo would welcome me on their lonely trip. The three of them were familiar with each other's lies, he said, laughing. Perhaps I would pretend to believe their stories and even laugh at their jokes.

I agreed to do both.

After that, Don Ramón, Pedro, and I drank beer and talked for almost an hour while Luis and Pablo retired to one of the back rooms with two of the girls.

When I rose to leave, I stumbled a little, and I realized that in a little less than sixty minutes I had, in an unsuccessful attempt to keep up with Don Ramón, drunk four bottles of beer, a good deal for a fifteen-year-old. Don Ramón had been there several hours already, drinking steadily, and on the way back to the hotel Pedro told me he would probably be sitting at that same table until morning, still drinking. By then, Pedro said, Don Ramón and most of the other llaneros in town would be blind drunk and have spent (or had stolen) their earnings for from six to nine months on the plains.

"These llaneros have a capacity for the beer," said Pedro, an observation I felt no inclination to argue against.

24

"But," Pedro went on, "he will be ready to leave on Monday morning as he promised. A llanero is a man of his word."

"What's the matter with Don Ramón's eyes?" I asked. As I had talked to him, his blank stare had unnerved me.

"Several years ago he was bitten by a rattlesnake," Pedro explained. "The poison affected his eyes. Soon he will be completely blind."

I shook Pedro's hand, thanked him, and, most important, pressed a few pesos into his hand. He smiled happily and once more offered to introduce me to one of his beautiful friends. Since the hour was late, he said, prices would have gone down.

I still refused his offer, a decision I later regretted. The floor of my room was not very soft.

At dawn on Monday it was raining; it was cold, and my back was covered with bites. By the time I'd dressed in the dark I was tempted to turn back. After all, I could still spend the rest of the summer lying in the sun and swimming in a pool in the outskirts of Bogotá, getting rested for what I knew was a tough year ahead. For just a moment it looked as if my father had been right; this "exploring foolishness" was too much for a fifteen-year-old who was fond of the comforts of life.

Then the proprietor of the hotel yelled up from downstairs, startling me and undoubtedly waking up any other guests foolish enough to be sleeping at five in the morning.

"Don Ramón is here," the proprietor yelled. "He says for you to hurry."

I hesitated for a few seconds, then picked up my gear and started down the stairs. From that time on there was no turning back.

When I got outside, Don Ramón, Luis, and Pablo gloomily climbed down from their horses and without a word loaded my gear on one of the two mules. Then, dripping water, Don Ramón handed me the reins of the fourth horse; I mounted, and we started off.

The streets of Villavicencio were deserted. The only sounds were the clatter of the hoofs and the splash of the rain as it struck the cobblestones. Lights were going on in the mud huts, now one, then a dozen, but it was still dark, and the rain continued. However, shortly after we entered the llanos the rain stopped abruptly; the sun came out, and there was a slight, cooling breeze.

Still none of us spoke. The plain stretched endlessly ahead, broken only by an occasional rolling hill or a matted patch of palm trees and undergrowth. I realized that for miles ahead there was probably not another human being except for a wandering Indian, a lonely rancher, a llanero or two.

Suddenly in the distance a huge ball of flame appeared against the sky; lightning had struck and was burning the dead leaves in a patch of jungle; then the fire spread into the surrounding dry grass. The grass on the llanos is sometimes hip deep and often taller than a man; when mature it is tough and wiry and hurts the mouths of the cattle. For that reason every August or September, during the dry season, the llaneros burn off the grass so that the cattle can eat tender new shoots in the spring. Nevertheless, the number of cattle which can be supported on each acre of land is extremely small.

Several times as we rode that morning a death moth flew by, *la cigarra de la muerte*. Each time I tried to avoid looking at what is surely the most repulsive insect in the world. It is a huge moth a little more than four inches long with large, mottled-gray wings, an oversized head which resembles a skull, and, just underneath. a long, evil-looking lancet. Don Ramón said that a man struck by the lancet invariably dies, hopelessly insane, within twenty-four hours.

A little later, as we approached a small stream, **Don Ramón** dismounted and looked carefully into the water. Then he motioned us ahead.

"There are no *tembladores* here," he said. "It is safe."

Tembladores, or electric eels, are ugly creatures about five slimy, wriggling feet long when grown. They lie on the bottoms of streams and when touched, by a human foot, say, send out a series of electrical charges which can and often do knock a man out. That is one of the many reasons it is madness to go swimming in one of the streams of the llanos or, for that matter, in most of the rivers of South America. Baron Alexander von Humboldt, the German naturalist who was one of the earliest and most famous explorers of the Amazon and the Orinoco, had a lot of trouble with the tembladores. In his account of his travels he writes that he drove his horses into an eel-infested stream. They screamed with terror. Some were immediately knocked unconscious and drowned. Others finally made it back to shore but then lay exhausted on the banks.

Luckily, for their fellow creatures anyway, the eels have very poorly developed teeth and can only eat animals small enough to be swallowed whole. On the other hand the Indians insist that the tail of the eel—about half its length—is delicious fried.

It rained intermittently throughout the day, and my clothes were never quite dry. When we started I was dressed the way I imagined an explorer should be, wearing a snappy green cork hat, well-pressed khaki trousers, and a freshly laundered shirt. My boots were ankle length and lightly polished, and I had a hunter's knife jauntily stuck in my belt.

By nightfall the snap and the press and the laundering were only memories. I was dripping with a sticky combination of perspiration and rain, and, when Don Ramón suggested that we make camp, I agreed. We stopped in a cleared spot not far from one of the greener patches of jungle. Pablo and Luis unloaded the mules, led them into the jungle, and returned with the mules carrying enough wood for a huge fire.

Don Ramón and I cooked the rice and beans and made the coffee. It was a delicious meal, and when we rolled up in our blankets, waiting for the fire to die down, I had a feeling I'd never had before but have many times since. I felt completely free.

It was a beautiful night. There were no clouds in the sky, only several million stars all close enough to touch. From the jungle came the song of a night bird, and the breeze rustled the leaves sleepily.

Just before I dropped off to sleep, Don Ramón said, "I guess you know that from Orocue you'll have to go down the Meta by boat." Orocue is a tiny village in the heart of the llanos.

"Why?" I wanted to know.

"Well," he said, slowly exhaling the smoke from his cigarette, "if you went by land, you'd have to cross the plains of the Guahibos. They kill any white man that comes within a hundred miles of their territory. They've even burned Orocue to the ground three times."

The Guahibos are among the least civilized tribes in South America. A few years ago, Don Ramón continued, a group of them killed fifty head of cattle he was helping graze. Then the Indians ran screaming into the darkness. An hour later Don Ramón and forty other armed men on fast horses started after the Guahibos. They were found in a patch of jungle on the edge of the llanos. After two hours of battle the Guahibos with their bows and arrows and primitive spears drove back the forty armed men.

It took a hundred men to rout them.

"It is difficult for a man on a horse to fight a Guahibo," Don Ramón went on. "He just vanishes when you are a few yards from him, and your bullets sink into the ground.

"One other time when I was driving a herd of cattle back to Villavicencio I came across five hundred of them—at least five hundred. I was all set to meet my maker when I got a wonderful idea. I stampeded the cattle and rushed them at the Indians. Scores were killed, and the rest ran. Even the wild bulls run when they see the Guahibos coming."

He paused for a moment, and I could hear the heavy snores of Luis and Pablo. They must have heard Don Ramón's stories dozens of times before, and I felt sure the number and ferocity of the Guahibos increased a little with each telling.

I started to yawn, then checked myself. "Another time," Don Ramón was saying, "I met with more than a thousand of them . . ."

I did not hear the end of the sentence. My sleeping bag at that moment seemed softer than anything the Simmons people ever put out, and I fell asleep.

The next day we traveled slowly, crossing rivers and streams, each of us searching not only for the electric eel but now for the far more dangerous sting ray and piranha. The sting ray is nearly square and has a tail like a whip which carries a poisoned spine capable of inflicting an extremely painful wound. It is not fatal, but on a later expedition one of my men who was affected suffered so much that he wanted to shoot himself. I had to take away his revolver.

The piranha or cannibal fish represents a different kind of

horror. At first glance it seems almost handsome. It is usually no more than eight inches to a foot in length, has a silver-gray back and a flaming orange belly. However, its teeth are saw-edged and needle-sharp, and the lower jaw protrudes so that when it snaps shut it is capable of a ripping action that can and often has removed a man's finger with a single bite. The piranha, sometimes called *caribe*, is attracted by the sight of blood. A few drops attracts hundreds of them, and a horse or a cow may be completely devoured within a few minutes.

At one point Don Ramón pointed out a school of these bloodthirsty fish swimming quietly in the water. Since neither we nor our animals had any wounds, it would, Don Ramón said, probably have been safe enough to cross there. Nevertheless we took no chances. We went a few hundred yards downstream.

"What would happen," I asked Don Ramón, "if a man fell into those waters back there?"

He shrugged philosophically.

"If he had no wounds, perhaps nothing," he said. "But if he had even the smallest gash, on his finger, say, he would not last more than a few minutes. Once one of my helpers cut his finger opening a can of sardines. The next day he fell off his horse crossing a stream. By the time we'd pulled him out, his stomach and head had holes the size of a fist. He died in less than two hours, and we buried him on the riverbank."

"In other words," I said, "these streams are no place for a man in red underwear to go swimming."

Don Ramón laughed—but only a little, and Luis and Pablo did not even smile.

The piranha is not a subject for jokes.

Occasionally in the jungle areas we saw armies of umbrella ants carrying pieces of leaves five and ten times as large as themselves.

On the plains we came across other ants building apartment houses which looked as if they might have been designed by Frank Lloyd Wright. They had terraces, each level a little smaller than the one below, and the houses were surrounded by spiral ramps for getting from one level to another.

Others made their homes in cone-shaped mounds of earth, sometimes four or five feet tall, and a third group lived in ball-like nests hidden in the forks of trees. By comparison with the piranha, the whole ant family seemed civilized and friendly.

Once in a while, too, we came across the jagged remains of missions, lonely, stark, and deserted, unhappy reminders of the days when the Jesuits took on the impossible task of civilizing most of South America.

We did not stop for noon chow; on an expedition I often don't. Instead I smoke a great many cigars to kill the hunger and, as a result, usually lose eight or ten of my 135 pounds before getting back home.

In the late afternoon we saw a ranch house in the distance, and we breathed easier. There are ranches at intervals throughout the llanos, always isolated, inevitably lonely, and often poverty-stricken. Plenty of land is available, and for the equivalent of $3000 you can buy a farm of ten by four kilometers. However, you must cultivate the land; otherwise it reverts to the government.

A former president of Colombia owns a ranch of several hundred square kilometers. However, the average is much smaller, and many of the ranchers—a word that in this context has a much more prosperous sound than it should—toil on their own plots of ground in the winter and spend their summers working for the large landowners. Naturally the best land is along the banks of streams or rivers, and bananas, coffee, yuca, and cacao are sometimes cultivated. Occasionally a little sugar cane is grown as well. Cattle grazing is almost always the most important source of income.

The ranchers come from everywhere. There are refugees from Germany and, more recently, from most of Eastern Europe. There are desperate men who have left the large cities of Colombia and Venezuela, pursuing wealth or a dream of freedom or, once in a while, escaping the law. They often succeed in evading it, but they seldom find wealth and much freedom. Their usual lot is backbreaking labor, beginning before dawn and lasting long after dusk, and their only reward is an often leaky roof over the heads of themselves and their families, and enough to eat. They often talk of returning to civilization once more, but they never do. As I've said, men seldom come back from the llanos, especially those who go there to live.

Our host that night was delighted to see us. The ranchers on the llanos always are. Any traveler is welcome day or night, and he is urged to stay as long as possible.

José's ranch was two kilometers square, and in addition to a few emaciated-looking cattle and some underfed pigs he grew a few vegetables, some coffee, and a bit of sugar cane. José, a small, painfully thin man with rounded shoulders, a pinched face, a large, aristocratic nose, a weak, girlish mouth and skin the reddish-brown color of highly polished mahogany, was a typical rancher. His ancestors probably included Spaniards, Indians, and Negroes, and numerous combinations of all three.

He grinned when he saw us, helped Luis and Pablo put up the horses and mules for the night, and then invited us in to meet his wife, who was reasonably pure Indian and at least twice his size, both in height and girth. She sighed happily and immediately put four more chipped plates on the roughhewn, unpainted table.

The house itself had one room, a dirt floor, a thatched roof, and three sides made of mud bricks; the fourth side was open. They had one son in his teens, who had left that morning for the next ranch—a good twenty miles away—to borrow some hunting dogs. A large jaguar had been killing the pigs, and José and his son were going on a jaguar hunt as soon as the boy returned with the dogs.

For a while after retiring that night—I had my hammock hung between two pillars—I considered staying on a few days to go on the hunt. The jaguar, whose sharp teeth are usually about the length of a man's little finger, is cornered by the dogs or forced up a tree. After that he is an easy target for the hunter. However, the cat frequently kills a dog or two first.

As a sport, a jaguar hunt had always seemed to me highly over-rated. So the next morning I set off again, thanking José and his wife, who said their farewells reluctantly. It would be six months before they got back to Villavicencio, and they might not see another human being except their son in the meantime.

As we rode off, José stood in the open field a little way from his desolate house, waving forlornly at us. He had come to the llanos from Bogotá to spend a year or so; he had hoped to save enough money to return and set himself up in business. That had been fifteen years before, and, although he was in his late thirties, he was already an old man, weary and defeated. Once in a while, he had said, he almost gave up hope, but, of course, there was his son. His son would not be a poverty-stricken and lonely rancher on the llanos. His son would be a businessman in Bogotá.

A few hours later, immediately after leaving a patch of jungle, we came to a narrow, gurgling stream. Halfway across, Pablo, who was a little ahead, jumped from his horse into the water, shouting angry and unprintable epithets.

When I reached him he was thrashing in the water, still shouting. A *macabrel* had, he shouted, flown from a tree branch and dropped near him. He was sure he had been bitten. The macabrel, whose bite is sometimes fatal, curls itself on a tree branch like a ball of shiny green yarn. According to Pablo, when someone passes underneath, the snake, which is usually two to three feet long with a one-inch diameter, flies through the air, lights on the man foolish enough to disturb its slumber, and bites. If, however, the man reaches the water before the snake, the bite will not be fatal.

Anyway, in Pablo's case it didn't matter. The macabrel had missed him and bitten only his sombrero.

Nevertheless he warned me to remember his advice; moreover he said that, if while I was barefoot I was ever bitten by a scorpion, all I had to do was to put on my shoes. Then I would recover immediately. He was not sure what would happen if I already had on my shoes.

We spent that night and the two following in the open, always stopping at night, usually pitching camp on the plains rather than in the jungle. Snakes are usually no real problem in the daytime. They are either asleep or dopey from the heat, but at night they can see well and hunt food. For that reason it is best, if possible, to be in the open.

On the tenth day after leaving Villavicencio—we had spent five nights in the open, five at ranch houses—we arrived at Orocue, a town of three hundred tormented souls on the Meta River.

Orocue will never be much of a tourist attraction. The streets are mud, and so are most of the houses. There are one or two brick mansions of two or three rooms, and a few of the more affluent inhabitants have aluminum or tin roofs. There seem to be almost as many pigs in town as people, and most families are of prodigious size. Then, too, almost everybody is related to almost everybody else, and the results of generations of inbreeding are often remarkable but frequently somewhat alarming.

Naturally there is a church and in addition to several smaller stores there is a single large general one with a long counter worn thin by generations of hagglers. The merchandise, all of which is brought in by horseback or dugout, includes a few bolts of colorful cloth, cotton and usually red or green or yellow or red and green and yellow. There are tiny mirrors, strings of cheap beads, earrings of the most intricate design, ribbons, huge bottles of the most aromatic perfume in the world, men's shirts, usually khaki, a few pairs of trousers, also khaki, belts, sombreros, cotton hats, and even a couple of pairs of men's shoes which must have been manufactured late in the nineteenth century. The storekeeper, who is also the postmaster and a man of considerable power and influence, confessed that he hadn't sold a pair in four or five years, but you never knew, he said, when a suddenly prosperous native might want to make an impression. Some of his male customers wore only loincloths, but others had at least one pair of trousers and a shirt, and only a few months before he had sold a pair of women's sandals, and he never knew when someone would come in for an aluminum pot or pan which, when highly polished, also served as a mirror.

In addition he sells weak lemonade and beer, lots of beer, and aguardiente, which is made from distilled sugar cane. All of his customers drank, he said, the majority of them often, some of them unceasingly. There is not much else to do in Orocue. Of course, there are women, a few nearly attractive, almost all of them available, a handful for a price, the majority for free.

The girls come in assorted colors, and there is no racial discrimination. This is partly because of a commendable tolerance and partly because it is almost impossible to tell what race anyone belongs to. Almost everybody belongs to several races. There are even a few Oriental traces discernible. How and from where I leave to the scientists.

I spent forty-eight hours in Orocue, and then I hitched a ride with six tame Guahibos, all of whom spoke a little Spanish but none of whom had anything to say to me except that they were going down the river and would be willing to accept more pesos than it was worth for a spot in their dugout. The dugout had been hewn out of a rough log, mostly by machete.

My six companions were dark, squat men, three in loincloths, three in trousers; they were uniformly ugly and uncommunicative, even with each other. I kept to myself, at least as much as was possible in the crowded dugout. I had a feeling that if I made a nuisance of myself they would just as soon cut off my head with their machetes and toss my torso into the Meta.

Don Ramón, Luis, and Pablo stayed behind in Orocue; they had a little more drinking to do before they went out to their herds. Each promised to look me up when he got to Bogotá, but they did not seem very hopeful. I was not sure if that was because they felt they wouldn't make the trip or because they thought I wouldn't survive mine. After all, I was now entering the country of untamed Guahibos.

I left Don Ramón in the village store, holding a bottle of beer in each hand, grinning at a very black girl who had her arms around his neck. His soft, milky eyes were sad, and I realized that in a very few months he would probably be completely blind and helpless. After a lifetime on the llanos he had neither family nor home nor money. Like so many other llaneros, there would be nothing for him to do except wander through the streets of Villavicencio or elsewhere, a useless derelict. I remembered his saying one night, "When the horse, he gets old and useless, he is shot, but with a man shooting is impossible, is that not so?"

In the dugout we averaged about fifteen miles a day, starting at dusk, stopping late in the afternoon. The Guahibos started to get tired, immediately and uniformly, exactly at four in the afternoon. In their inadequate Spanish they explained that their backs ached; their arms were tired from paddling; their heads had absorbed too much sun and too much rain, and, besides, they wanted to stop. The first few days I tried to urge them on, but it was useless. They did not have watches, but they knew when it was four o'clock. We made camp by the bank of the river, and I shared my rations with them. Their appetites were in no way affected by their fatigue.

On the second day, as we came to a turn in the river, we saw a huge boa on the bank with a *babilla* it had just strangled in its coils. The babilla is a thin, small alligator seldom more than four feet long and with a thin, narrow mouth. The boa, which must have been twenty feet in length, suddenly grew shorter at least by half. At the same time its girth doubled. Then, with a single gulp, it swallowed the babilla.

After that the boa slid into the river, and, except for the distended bulge of the babilla in its middle, submerged itself.

The Guahibos seemed to get a little paler as they watched, and I know I did. We proceeded slowly, holding onto the branches which hung over the water's edge and pushing the dugout forward.

Suddenly there was an anguished scream from the stern. Without thinking I jumped into the water and started swimming ashore. So did five of the Guahibos. When we turned we saw that a second boa had slithered into the dugout and was coiling around the Indian who had screamed.

37

From onshore we saw the Indian pull out his knife and begin jabbing at the snake. We yelled instructions, each of them, I'm sure, different, but if he heard he paid no attention. Instead, he continued to jab with his knife, and somehow managed to get the boa's tail in his mouth. Then he bit hard.

It is an Indian legend—at least I had thought until that moment that it was legend—that if you are able to bite the snake's tail hard enough, it will let go. I don't know whether it was that or the numerous knife wounds, but the boa, after a few tortured moments, uncoiled, and the shivering, terrified Guahibo got out of the boat and swam ashore.

Meantime the dugout, with the boa as well as our supplies and all of my gear inside, continued to drift down the river.

I pleaded; I argued, and I offered all the pesos I had for one of the Indians to go swimming after it, but they all quite sensibly refused. A wounded boa, they said, is the most dangerous of living creatures.

Finally I gave up, and we all ran along the shore, praying that the dugout would not drift into midstream, where we were sure it would be lost forever.

A few minutes later the now visibly wounded boa slid out of the canoe and into the water. As it did so it forced the dugout farther away from shore. A few minutes later it reached the center of the river and disappeared from view.

I don't know how the Guahibos felt; they kept their emotions to themselves. I was scared. One of the Guahibos said that the nearest settlement was not far away, but I had already learned that his sense of distance was unreliable. I did not know whether he meant that it was ten miles or a hundred. Meantime we had no sleeping bags, no hammocks, and no food of any kind.

What's more, I had no gun and my hunting knife was on the dugout.

Also I had left my matches and my cigarette lighter on board, a mistake I have never made since.

However, the Guahibos told me not to worry. The dugout would reappear eventually, they said. It was simply a matter of waiting. Since that is the native approach to all problems, I was not much encouraged.

We walked on in silence for a few minutes, each of us keeping one eye on the river for the missing dugout, the other on the thick undergrowth. Then, faintly at first but gradually much louder, we heard the sound of what might have been several hundred castanets. A moment later our noses were assailed—and no other word will do—by a nauseous odor that rapidly increased in intensity. Without a word we each chose a nearby tree and started climbing. A few seconds later a herd of at least two hundred peccaries appeared.

The peccary is a small, bad-tempered wild pig; it ranges in length from a foot and a half to three feet, is usually a grayish black in color and has a pair of short, ominously sharp tusks that grow straight down. It uses the tusks to dig up roots and to tear out the entrails of jaguars; in addition it eats snakes and lizards and just about anything else it can find, dead or alive, which probably accounts for its undeniably offensive odor. I'm told that if the wind is right you can pick up the scent a mile away. The peccary travels in herds of up to four and five hundred. Although, if captured young, it can be made into a satisfactory and not too smelly pet, its sole charm when wild is that in vibrating its lower jaw its tusks rub together and produce the castanet-like sound, which is both rhythmic and terrifying.

A herd of peccaries will attack a man just because he happens to get in the way. Luckily, however, they cannot climb trees.

As I looked down on the herd I remembered that in Orocue

the storekeeper had told me that a peccary hunt was one of the favorite sports for the townsmen—aside from drinking and women, of course. It goes like this. A group of horsemen rounds up a herd of peccaries. Then, after the alarm is sounded, the peccaries are driven into the village square. After that the "sport" gets underway. From every doorway and window on the square the villagers start shooting, and that night every cooking pot in town has at least one or two peccaries in it.

The taste, the storekeeper said, is delicious; he compared it to the best *filet mignon*, although, he continued, he'd never eaten a filet mignon. Yes, he admitted, the square did get a little messy during the "hunt"; there was quite a bit of peccary blood smeared about, but in a few days, he said, the birds and dogs had cleaned it all up.

However, even if we had been armed, I don't think any of the seven of us would have wanted to take on that herd of peccaries, and, after what was probably no more than half an hour but seemed longer, the wild pigs disappeared, and we stretched out on the ground, hungry, cold, and, in my case anyway, frightened and discouraged. I don't think I slept more than half an hour during the whole night.

The next morning, breakfastless and sleepless, we trudged on. There was still no dugout in sight.

The Guahibos by now seemed to be a little less philosophical than they had been the night before, and every once in a while one of them would turn around and, if he thought I wasn't looking, glare at me. It was clear that they now blamed me rather than the boa for the loss of their dugout. Occasionally another would mutter what must have been an obscenity. At other times a third would make an ominous gesture in my direction.

However, I pretended to be extremely cheerful; I whistled and sang and offered cigars to everyone. No one took any.

We must have been walking for five or six hours, and all of us were near the breaking point when, as we rounded a sharp bend, we saw the dugout, looking calm and ordered, tangled in some bushes by the side of the river.

The Guahibos grinned and said something like, "We told you so." I simply grinned, and we all climbed in, ate a shamefully heavy lunch—for instance, we each had three helpings of beans—and then paddled on.

A few hours later we came to the settlement, which was no more than an irregular circle cleared in the jungle with half a dozen thatched-roof huts made of mud, but the river there was calm and clear, and the trees seemed taller and greener. It was a beautiful spot and since I was in no hurry I decided to stay on for a while. I said good-by to the Guahibos and paid them off. They did not seem particularly unhappy to leave me. They probably thought I brought them bad luck since in a single day we had met up with two boas and a herd of peccaries and lost, if only temporarily, their painfully constructed dugout.

I hung my hammock in a small lean-to next to one of the huts. I preferred sleeping there bceause the huts were without exception constantly filled with smoke from the cooking fires built inside.

For the next few days I slept, and I read, and I swam, and I ate. But mostly I listened, and I watched. There was a toothless crone who remembered or said she remembered eating part of a white man when she was a girl; her father and mother had both been cannibals, she said proudly and a little nostalgically. There were a few boys preparing to go on their first hunt; there were men returning home with fish freshly caught and monkeys newly slain; there were women preparing the endless round of meals; there were crying babies and tiny girls bathing tinier brothers. One of the illusions about the Indian—or any so-called savage— is that he is dirty. With rare exceptions he is quite the opposite. Since he almost always lives near a river, he bathes several times daily. It is only when he becomes half civilized that he stops washing.

Life in the settlement was quiet, monotonous, I suppose, but also fascinating. For one thing, until the night of the party I didn't hear a single quarrel.

On the morning of the third day a launch arrived with two traders on their way to Puerto Carreño, the frontier village on the edge of the llanos which was my destination. However, I decided not to join them; they were planning too many stops along the way. One of the traders was a rough, dark man with tiny yellow teeth, a long scar across his entire left cheek, and a murderous look in his eye; the other was an athletically built young man who laughed a great deal for no apparent reason.

A few hours after the traders arrived two canoes filled with Guahibos moored nearby. In one boat were six girls, young, well built, and for sale. The two traders bought all six, in exchange for a few machetes, a couple of bolts of red cotton cloth, and, most important, half a dozen bottles of aguardiente. The Guahibos often sell their women, temporarily anyway. The two traders would keep the girls for a few days, maybe a week or longer; then the girls would be put off the launch somewhere along the riverbank, and they would walk back home. They don't seem to mind such treatment or, if they do, know better than to complain. Besides, they are used to promiscuity of all kinds. The Guahibos are not immoral people. They are simply without morals of any kind.

42

I found out more about that at the party that evening. I don't
know what the celebration was about. I doubt if it was about
anything except the fact that aguardiente was available. Everybody in the settlement bought at least one bottle from the traders,
and I contributed two to the general collection. In addition I
bought a pair of ornate, dangling red glass earrings for María, the
dark, attractive fifteen-year-old who did my laundry and cooking.

That night every man in the settlement got drunk. There were
half a dozen fights; machetes and knives were drawn frequently;
there was some bloodshed, not much. Most participants were
soon too drunk to do each other much harm. There was a good
deal of retiring to the bushes outside with whatever member of
the opposite sex was available, and there was some increasingly
awkward dancing to the accompaniment of two guitars and a pair
of maracas. Considerably after midnight, during what promised
to be a nearly fatal knife fight over an elderly woman of twenty-
odd, I sneaked off to my hammock, took off my clothes, and
immediately fell asleep.

A few minutes later I awakened, realizing that something soft
had fallen next to me. It was María.

I hadn't realized how very grateful she was for the earrings.

The next afternoon during siesta time I was lying in my hammock
reading. It was at that time of day when all life in the llanos and
jungle of necessity stops. The sun was beating relentlessly down;
there was not even the hint of a breeze, and from the jungle across
the river I saw rising vapors of steam. From somewhere in one of
the huts a baby cried; a mother said the equivalent of "hush," and
my book dropped to the ground.

In another moment I would have been asleep except that from
down the river I heard the sound of paddles striking the sides of

a dugout. A feminine voice laughed, and then there was a great deal of giggling. Finally the paddling stopped, and there was a splash of water and more giggling. Then a soft voice in a loud stage whisper said something, and a second voice whispered back.

After that there was a moment of silence and then the sound of running feet. I was about to get up enough energy to open my eyes when something banged hard against the back of my hammock, upsetting it and landing me on the floor, face down.

I sat up. I was surrounded by half a dozen terrified Indian girls, none of them more than in her early teens, all on tiptoe, all looking down on me, expecting immediate and painful punishment. They had undoubtedly dared someone of their number to upset my hammock.

I started to rise. Then I saw, fallen against one of the posts which held up the roof of my lean-to, the girl who had stumbled. It is difficult to know exactly what I thought at that moment. I gasped and sat there on the ground for all of what must have been a full minute. I was unable to move.

Although she became even more beautiful later, Catani was at that moment one of the most magnificent-looking creatures I have ever seen. She was fourteen, and it took only a glance to see that she was not an Indian. Her skin was burnt red-brown by the sun, but it was smooth and unblemished. Her hair, which had a natural curl, was pulled back from her forehead, and it was raven black. Her eyes were large, brown, and at that moment frightened. Her nose was straight and delicate, an aristocratic nose, I thought; her lips were full, wide, and already sensuous. Her figure was already fully developed, her breasts small and firm. She wore a dirty red cotton dress, which was much too short and tight for her and was slightly torn across one breast, and she was barefoot.

I have always felt that there are more beautiful women on Fifth

Avenue in New York City in the late afternoon of a weekday than anyplace else in the world at any hour of the day or night. If I had seen this girl on Fifth at 5 P.M. of a Wednesday, I would have turned and watched her; I would unquestionably have followed her, too. But this was not New York; this was a desolate settlement in the middle of the Meta River, which runs through the Colombian llanos.

To repeat, I gasped.

She looked at me and hurriedly tried to cover the tear in her dress with one hand. I imagined that men had been reaching for her ever since she was a little girl. Then she rose and ran out of the lean-to, followed by the other Indian girls.

By that time everybody else in the settlement had been awakened by the noise. Most of the Indians had rushed out of their huts to talk to the girls.

I followed them, keeping my eye on the girl in the torn dress; I could not have done anything else.

I walked up to Simón, the old man whose hut was next to my lean-to, nodded toward the girl, and asked who she was.

"Her name," he said, "is Catani. She is the daughter of a foreigner who lives down the river about half an hour from here. I believe that her mother died of a snakebite some years back."

I was later to learn more, much more, about Catani, but for the moment that was enough. I kept watching her, repeating the name to myself, wondering.

"Catani." It was a beautiful name.

A few minutes later she and the other girls climbed in the dugout and paddled away. At that moment I felt like jumping in another canoe and paddling after her, but I didn't. I've often wondered what would have happened if I had, and once, years later, I asked her. At first she laughed; then she turned away, and

45

I felt for a moment that she was crying. But I couldn't be sure. I could never be sure, and as I've said that was years later and was far away from the banks of the Meta.

The next morning a second launch arrived on its way to Puerto Carreño, and I went on with it.

By that time my expedition was nearly over; Puerto Carreño is, after all, only a slightly larger, somewhat less sleepy version of Orocue. There is a customs house, but otherwise there is what might be the same two or three brick houses, the same handful with tin and aluminum roofs, the same square, the same general store with perhaps the same two pairs of men's shoes and possibly the same populated lemonade.

A few days later I was on my way back to Bogotá, ten pounds lighter, several dozen shades darker, somewhat wiser, considerably more than two months older, and incredibly happier.

That winter at the New York Military Academy I made the mistake of mentioning Catani at chow one day. The future officers and gentlemen hooted.

"There goes Acebes again," one said. "Next he'll be telling us about the time he was chased up a tree by a herd of wild pigs."

"Or how he was *almost* strangled by a boa," said another.

"Or maybe about how he *nearly* went on a jaguar hunt," said a third.

After lights-out that night I thought of Catani until I fell asleep.

2

It was summer again, and there was a restlessness in the air.

In the years that had passed since my expedition into the llanos,

I had completed two years at the Massachusetts Institute of Technology, and I had another two years to go before receiving my bachelor of science in mechanical engineering. I had also participated in a war, and I had a private's first class stripe, a discharge button, and the only medal to which I was entitled, one attesting that my conduct in the U. S. Army had been good.

But it had not been much of a war for me. I spent one year, eight months, and nineteen days of it in the United States; I went through basic training five times and at least a dozen times was threatened with a court martial for writing direct to the War Department to request overseas service. I finally got to Germany in March 1945, just in time to take part in the final battles against the nazis.

The year that followed in Germany had been pleasant enough, but after my discharge at Fort Devens I hurried to Boston, made arangements for my final two years at M.I.T., and then flew to Bogotá and Madeline, who was—and, for that matter, still is—the most beautiful woman in all the world. She was a Bostonian; I had met her at one of the last parties I attended before going into the Army, and we were married on my first furlough. She had spent the rest of the war with my family in Bogotá.

Now I was home once more, and it was time for me to settle down. I was a husband, and I was the father of a daughter, and I needed to have a sense of responsibility. At least everybody said I did. My father said it, and my brother said it, and my aunt said it, and Madeline said it. I agreed. I really ought to settle down, and I must develop a sense of responsibility.

For a couple of weeks I did. I went down to my father's office every morning at nine, and I shuffled some papers and made some phone calls. I wore a blue serge suit, and I began to develop a slight paunch. I talked knowingly of profit and loss in the textile business. I even spoke of opening a branch factory or two.

Unfortunately, in planning for expansion, which was just then both impractical and impossible, I got out a huge map of Colombia, and my eyes kept straying to an area I'd always dreamed of exploring, the Vaupés River, home of the mysterious Macú Indians.

It really wasn't much of a trip, I kept telling myself, a five-hour flight by Catalina to Mitú, a village on the Vaupés near the border of Brazil. After that I could pick up a couple of guides and proceed down the river to the Macú territory. Why, I needn't be gone more than two or three, maybe four or five, possibly six weeks; after all, I did need a vacation, and it wouldn't take any longer than a North American hunting trip to, say, Canada. Why, it was nothing at all.

I was quiet at dinner that night, and during the evening I wasn't much interested in the thermodynamics text I was supposedly studying, boning up for the next year at M.I.T.

About nine o'clock Madeline, who seemed to be reading a novel, looked up and said, "When are you leaving?"

"Leaving?" I said. "Leaving for where?"

"I don't know where," said Madeline, smiling. "I just know you're thinking about another expedition."

"Don't be silly," I said.

"I don't know what you're talking about," I said.

"I'm studying," I said.

She continued to smile. "Look," she said, "before we got married, you told me about the exploring bug that bit you, and you said you'd probably outgrow it. I said you probably never would, and I told you I wouldn't stand in your way when you wanted to go someplace."

She rose, came over and kissed me, and then said, "I haven't changed my mind. Now where are you going this time?"

48

"Well," I began, and I told her.

Two days later I was on the Catalina, flying south from Bogotá.

As the plane slithered across the smooth waters of the Vaupés, half a dozen dugouts started out from shore, each bearing a handful of Indians, the men dressed only in the briefest of loincloths, the women—most of them girls—in thin, short, tight cotton dresses.

They waited eagerly for the doors of the plane to open. Its arrival is the most important event in their lives. When the water is high it comes once a week, bringing merchandise and an occasional passenger to Mitú, returning to Bogotá with a cargo of rubber. In the dry season as many as three or four months may pass without a single plane.

I was the only passenger on that trip, and as I stepped into one of the dugouts the girls giggled and whispered to themselves; the men looked at me expectantly. The unending heat began to beat down on me immediately, the heat that I had missed as I shivered my way across postwar Germany, cold, beaten, and sullen.

I looked across at the green, mossy banks of the river and at the long, narrow border of palm-roofed huts. For the first time since returning from Europe I felt relaxed. I knew that here there had been no war. Here there was only the river, the sky, the jungle, and a people too lazy or too wise or too foolish to drop bombs on each other.

The village of Mitú has probably never had a census. I would guess it has a population of about 300, of which 290 are Indians, most of the rest a mixture of bloods. There are three hardworking, lonely young missionaries, two policemen, three clerks, one secretary, and the comisario.

49

The main street is three blocks long. Except for the church and the *comisaría*, a long, two-story wooden structure with open corridors running around its perimeter on both the first and second floors, the buildings are mostly made of mud and have thatched roofs.

Only a Model-T Ford distinguishes Mitú from scores of other jungle villages throughout South America. The Model-T was brought overland from Bogotá in a three months' journey, with Indian guides chopping a now non-existent path through the jungle. The truck is used to transport raw rubber from one end of the main street to the other. Otherwise it rusts in the sun and the rain.

The Indians laughed happily and started paddling the dugout toward shore.

Señor Cayzedo, the comisario, was not on hand to greet me, and when I knocked on the door of his headquarters there was no answer; I shouted, and there was still no answer. Then I knocked again, even more loudly, and after a few moments a bent, toothless Indian crone who was barefoot and whose torn dress had been patched many times came out of the building and motioned for me to follow her. We went up the outside steps, and she knocked at a door on the second floor.

A slightly blurred voice shouted for us to come in. Three men were sitting at a cluttered table which also served as a desk, a bottle of aguardiente between them. Although it was still morning the bottle was already half empty, and I could see, from looking at the three men, that they had consumed it all—and possibly more—that day.

I introduced myself and asked which of the men was Señor Cayzedo. A thin man of medium height who was probably no more than forty-five but appeared older, looked up and nodded. I handed him a card from Señor Camacho Ramírez, then head of the Colombian Department of National Territories. Cayzedo took the card and without looking at it put it in the pocket of his rumpled jacket.

"There is a message on the other side," I explained. He took the card, glanced at it, and returned it to his pocket, visibly unimpressed.

"Have a drink," he said, pouring a heavy slug of the liquor into a glass. I took the glass, wished good health, first, to Señor Cayzedo, then to a wiry man of about thirty-five with a bushy mustache who was introduced as the chief of police, and finally to a young trader in a khaki shirt and trousers, with a hat on the table beside him.

Then I drank all of the aguardiente in a single gulp, which impressed the three men.

The comisario invited me to sit down, first pouring me another drink. He was, he explained, a very busy man. The next comisaría was four months away by dugout and over jungle footpaths. I could understand, then, he went on, that the administration of so vast an area was an overwhelming burden. I said that I could. There were many reports to write, many papers to sign, much advice to be given. There were rubber traders who had to be told which Indians to hire and which trails to follow, and then, too, there was always trouble with the Indians. They were, he said, like children, and they had to be punished when necessary.

Thus, said Señor Cayzedo, it was only natural that he and the chief and the young trader there occasionally take a few minutes off for a brief drink. Was that not so?

I said that it was the most natural thing in the world.

When Señor Cayzedo learned that I had once lived in Madrid,

51

he was delighted and told me that he had a son studying medicine in Valladolid, Spain, where my father was born. Such a remarkable coincidence called for several more drinks.

When I explained that I wanted to go down the Vaupés to see the Macues, the three men laughed uproariously. The Macues were scattered and inaccessible, they said; the river in that direction was always arduous and often unnavigable; I would, in all probability, never make it. Why, instead, did I not take a nice little trip up the river—fifteen days at most, round trip—to see the waterfalls of Yuruparí, the most beautiful in all the world?

I declined politely. Scenery, I said, didn't interest me much. I wanted to visit the Macú Indians.

But why the Macues? the chief wanted to know. Surely all Indians were alike. There were Indians right here in Mitú, and there was a very fascinating group in a settlement only half an hour away. Why not look at them?

"I want," I said slowly, a little angry by now, "to look at the Macues. That is why I am here. Can you help me find a guide?"

Señor Cayzedo smiled. "We will discuss it," he said, and we did.

After a surprisingly delicious lunch served by Señora Cayzedo, a plump, pleasant-looking woman who wanted to know what kind of dresses the women in Bogotá were wearing this season, we debated the matter some more, over a second bottle of aguardiente. By suppertime I had made my point. Señor Cayzedo agreed to help me, and we had several more drinks to celebrate our decision.

Later in the evening another policeman joined us; he had come to Mitú from a jungle outpost, a day or more away, where he was stationed alone. It was one of six such outposts covering an area of the Vaupés almost four hundred miles long. He explained that he had arrived only a few weeks before. In two months, three at most, he said, he would request a transfer back to Bogotá.

Señor Cayzedo looked at the eager, unlined brown face and patted the policeman on the shoulder. Then the señor shrugged sadly.

"Once," he said, "I had such dreams. Once long ago."

He paused, and when he continued his voice was more cheerful. "But now I know," he said, "if you do not leave before the first month is over, you will never leave. I have never known it to fail."

"But they don't even give us anything to work with," said the policeman. "The roof of my outpost is falling in. To prop it up, I have to go into the jungle myself to cut new poles."

Señor Cayzedo smiled knowingly. "In a short while," he said, "you will have a young Indian girl to share your loneliness. Soon after that you yourself will take down the poles in your outpost to make the roof more crooked. That is the way of the jungle."

The policeman was not convinced, but he did agree to another drink, a strong one this time, he said.

I didn't sleep very well that night. Scores of rats scurried down the corridors and across the floor of my room in a never-ending pursuit of insects, and there were at least three bats circling overhead, one of which kept making passes directly in front of my face. Finally I rose, went into the corridor, picked up a thin stick, and in a technique I had learned from the Indians vibrated it rapidly in the air. The sound attracted the bat and as it neared the stick I struck it twice, and it fell to the floor. The other bats stayed away from my face after that, but did not leave the room. The rats did not retire until after daybreak.

53

I spent the next three days exploring Mitú, chatting with the dedicated young priests, who also seemed to have a resigned feeling that their God and their fate would never allow them to return to civilization. I also met a pleasant young Indian girl who in the United States might have been an exhibit in a side show; here she was not considered particularly unusual, although she was nicknamed The Map. Her face was splotched with alternate light and dark areas which, if you were properly imaginative, might have been said to look like the continents and oceans of the world. She was suffering from a skin disease quite common among many tribes of the Amazon basin.

One evening I also met the only Negro in Mitú or, in fact, for many miles in any direction. In talking to me he kept referring to himself and me as "us whites."

When I politely pointed out that his skin was as black as a moonless night, he winked and grinned at me.

"True," he said, "my skin is black, but here in Mitú there are only whites and Indians. I am not an Indian. Therefore, I am white."

"But what if you leave Mitú for the interior?" I asked.

He winked again and shrugged.

"In that case," he said, "I would become a Negro again."

There is a handful of general stores in Mitú, small, cluttered, and disordered; they stay in business by selling merchandise at exorbitant prices to the rubber traders in the area. The traders are, in many ways, very much like the llaneros; at an early age they are invariably bent and broken men, invariably poverty-stricken, invariably dreaming of escape and realizing they never will.

The wild rubber in the jungles surrounding Mitú is gathered over a six-month period of the year, and two traders in partnership, working long hours with the help of a handful of Indians may, if they are lucky, make a thousand dollars each. By the time they have been on a couple of drunks and paid their past-due bills at one of the general stores, they seldom have enough left over to take care of themselves and their families through the six remaining months.

The Indians have an even worse time, although conditions have improved considerably since the days late in the nineteenth and early in this century when several thousand Indians working in the wild rubber areas died every year, some of malnutrition, some of overwork; many were murdered. This was particularly true in the vicinity of the Putumayo River on the border between Colombia and Peru. There the Peruvian Amazon Company for years worked Indians day and night, paying them nothing and giving them only enough food to keep them alive. They were robbed of their crops, their women, and their children; they were refused medical treatment, and if they rebelled their homes were burned to the ground. In some cases ears, fingers, arms, or legs were cut off; some had their bodies cut to pieces by machetes, the various parts thrown to the dogs as food; others were crucified, with their heads hanging down. Sometimes a child would be grabbed by the feet and, before its parents' eyes, a supervisor would bash out the child's brains on the nearest wall or rock. The old were automatically killed when they could no longer work.

In less sober moments the overseers would douse an Indian with kerosene, then set him afire, having another drink as the man screamed, laughing at his agony, making bets as to how long he would continue screaming. During other drinking bouts—of which there were a great many—the overseers would, for additional amusement, discharge their guns at the men, women, and children; sometimes only two or three were killed.

55

Now, of course, the traffic in Indian slavery has ended—officially, anyway, and murder for amusement is forbidden. Nevertheless, the annihilation of the Indian continues.

During the six-month rubber-gathering season he abandons his crops, and, since his pay is almost non-existent during the idle season, he seldom has enough food for himself and his family.

At that point, in order to be sure of having a worker (not a slave, understand) for the next season, the trader advances the Indian—at no more than a fifty-per-cent markup—enough merchandise to get through the winter.

Naturally the Indian has to pay his debt before he can work for another trader. Most Indians never work themselves out of debt, and, when they are too old to gather rubber and to cultivate their crops, they often die of malnutrition or of tuberculosis.

Thus the Indian is born and dies hating the white man and blaming him for all the troubles of his people. Not surprisingly, he sometimes strikes back.

The day before I left Mitú two policemen and two Indian deputies arrived from the interior with a handsome, husky boy of seventeen who had just committed one of the bloodiest crimes in the history of the Vaupés.

The murderer, who looked at me with obvious hate, grinned and laughed when he described his crime to the two Indian deputies. He sounded as if he were describing a soccer game he had won.

He had been hired as one of four paddlers by a white trader who for years had been working along the Vaupés and the Inirida rivers. One night, while the trader and his pregnant Indian wife were sleeping near the edge of the Vaupés, the young murderer arose and beat the trader to death with a stick. When the wife awakened she screamed with terror and ran to the river, throwing herself in. The murderer jumped in after her and dragged her out by the hair. Then he took her husband's machete and cut her body into four nearly equal pieces. These he threw into the river. After that he chopped out the trader's intestines and tossed them and the rest of the body into the river too.

The other three paddlers rushed to the nearest settlement and returned with the two Indian deputies, who captured the murderer.

Just before the two deputies and the two policemen marched the murderer off to the comisaría, he turned toward me, scowled, and with a sneer spat directly into my face.

"He hates all whites," one of the policemen said apologetically. "He has told his tribe that they are no good and that they must all be killed."

Later I learned that the young Indian's grandfather had been murdered by the early rubber traders.

On the fourth morning after my arrival, with the help of Señor Cayzedo and the entire officialdom of Mitú, I was ready to leave on my expedition. If I'd made the preparations myself, I could probably have left on the second morning.

My guide was Pedro Pablo, a wise and compact little rubber trader who had been going up and down the river for years; he knew every turn in it, every rapid, every rock, and every indentation along the shore. With him he brought four grinning and nearly naked Kubeo Indians. They said they were glad to meet me.

I doubted that. It was 3 A.M., an hour at which no one is ever glad to meet anyone else. Besides, it was raining, and it was cold. Both Pedro and I were wearing huge black rubber ponchos, and in the darkness we must have looked like large, evil bats. None of us spoke as my gear was loaded into the large, two-ton *batelo* Pedro was taking to his plantation. The batelo is simply a huge canoe; a woven palm-leaf roof is built over one end to protect the occupants from the sun and rain; there is plenty of space for cooking and sleeping on board, and, finally and most important, the batelo is stable enough to navigate most rapids, a characteristic we had plenty of opportunity to test in the next few days.

By dawn we were loaded, and the rain had stopped. The cloudless sky was a cobalt blue, the river slightly darker, and the red ball of sun in the east gave off a comforting warmth.

From shore someone shouted, "Bon voyage," Pedro gave the signal, and we pushed off. I found myself singing the song of the llaneros again; I was leaving the half-civilization of Mitú. From here on in I would be in Indian country.

We reached the first rapid within half an hour after we started. Then we unloaded the batelo; the Kubeos lifted the supplies to their backs, and Pedro and I dragged the canoe along close to shore until the rapids had been passed. After that we reloaded and were on our way again—but not for long. In a one-hundred-and-fifty-mile stretch we came across sixty-five rapids, all sizes, all shapes, all dangerous. Very few of them could be navigated, and through practice we soon became very proficient in loading and unloading the batelo.

We also realized that except for Pedro's knowledge and skill any one of the rapids might have meant the end of all of us.

Several times we had to stop to pick up a pilot to guide us over a particularly treacherous spot, but when we arrived at the infamous Uacurabá Rapid the pilot was not around. So Pedro and I got out of the boat and went to a large hut a few yards up the shore. Inside we found a muscular young Indian lying on his hammock with a piece of bark cloth tied around his head. He groaned and writhed pitifully, not even opening his eyes as we entered.

"What's the matter, *compadre?*" asked Pedro.

"I was pregnant," said the young Indian.

"And when did you give birth?" Pedro asked.

"Only last night," said the Indian, groaning again.

Pedro's dark face flushed angrily. "Listen to me, damn you," he said. "You're not sick at all. Now you get out of that hammock and take us over the rapid." He fingered his pistol ominously, and the Indian, clutching his stomach, rose and carefully untied the bark cloth, neatly laying it on the hammock. Then he took us down to the river, groaning every step or so.

After we passed the rapid we let the Indian off, and he limped back to his hut, still groaning, still clutching his stomach. Pedro was convinced it was an act, but then Pedro had never heard of psychosomatic pains.

Throughout the area of the Vaupés, after the mother bears the child, the father takes to his hammock. He ties a piece of bark cloth around his head, lies down, and starts shouting with pain. He groans for three days and three nights. Naturally the mother has to be up and around to nurse him through his ordeal. She doesn't have time to be sick.

When she is ready to give birth, she simply goes into the jungle and has her baby alone. She breaks the umbilical cord with her teeth. If she has twins, she chokes one. If she feels she already has too many children and doesn't want the new one, she strangles it. If the child is deformed, she kills it, too. If not, she takes the new baby back to her hut, helps her husband into his hammock, and then paints the baby with red spots. This protects it from marauding jaguars.

At the end of three days the father rises from his hammock of pain and accompanies the mother as she carries the baby down to the river. There she makes a fire, and when it has died down he helps her throw the cinder ashes into the river, making a huge circle. Then all three bathe inside the circle. The ashes protect the child from the monsters of the water, particularly the anaconda.

After the ceremony the mother, carrying the baby and accompanied by the father, returns to the hut. The father immediately goes back to his hammock, and for the next thirty days he does no strenuous work, drinks almost no alcohol, and has no intercourse. If he did, the umbilicus of the baby would fall off.

Shortly before dusk we came to a small circular clearing in which there was a single Indian hut or *maloca*, housing perhaps half a dozen families. We passed such settlements every ten or fifteen miles along the riverbank. They never included more than a few huts and usually, as in this case, only one.

As we approached the maloca, one of the Kubeos whispered something to a second, who burst into loud, delighted laughter. Then he passed the word along to a third, and, finally, all four were giggling like children. I've read that humor is the special characteristic of the civilized man, but I've yet to meet an Indian who didn't find a great many things humorous—a special swirl in the current of the river, the shape of a cloud, the gnarled trunk of a tree, the appearance of a sloth hanging upside down, and always me, especially me. The Indians laugh at the way I talk, dress, sleep, and eat; they make fun of the way I tie my shoelaces, go to the toilet, and comb my hair; they find my smoking cigars hilarious.

In this case, however, I wasn't the joke, but, when I asked Pedro what was, he merely grinned and shook his head.

"You'll see," he said. "Just watch."

Finally, the Kubeos eased the batelo up to shore, and all of us except one Kubeo got out and climbed up the bank toward the clearing. The men of the maloca were still hunting in the jungle, and the women were preparing the evening meal outside.

They looked up at us, shrugged, and went on with their work. We stood around for a few moments while one of my guides surveyed them; then he walked up to one of the youngest and easily the prettiest girl of the lot, grabbed her wrist, and, before she had a chance to react, threw her over his shoulder and started running.

For a moment the girl was too surprised to do anything, but in a few seconds she was kicking and screaming, biting and scratching. Her kidnaper chortled with delight and continued running toward the river. So did the rest of us, although I still wasn't sure what was happening.

In a few seconds the men of the maloca ran out of the jungle. As soon as they saw what was going on, they rushed for us, also shouting and screaming. By that time we were back on board the batelo, and the girl, who was fighting, was being held down on the bottom of the boat.

The men of the maloca tried to grab onto the sides of the batelo, but we beat them off with our paddles and in a moment the seven of us were once more in the middle of the river, rapidly paddling downstream, Pedro, myself, the four Kubeos, and our new passenger. When she sat up, I could see that her kidnaper had not made a mistake. She had a round, firm body that soon would become a little coarse, but now was exactly right; her hair was short and straight, her features well matched. As she sat up in the boat she frowned and said something to the Kubeos, who laughed.

"She says," Pedro explained, "that she hopes her bridegroom will be handsome."

61

Then he pointed out that among the Kubeos what I had just seen was the first step of a marriage. This girl, he went on, would be taken to the maloca of my guides. There she would be turned over by her kidnaper to his brother or a friend.

The practice is a common one, he said. The girl would probably be delighted with her husband—or at least would pretend to be. If, however, she was miserable and admitted it, she would be given to one of the other men of the maloca, and this would continue until she found someone she liked.

In a few weeks, Pedro went on, or a few months, perhaps, the girl's relatives would probably send someone to the groom's maloca to steal a bride. If no unmarried girls were available, a present would be necessary.

However, Pedro concluded, there were usually plenty of unmarried girls in every maloca.

Two days later, shortly before we reached Pedro Pablo's ranch, we dropped the Kubeos and the girl.

When she saw her groom standing near the maloca, she sighed happily and whispered to Pedro that, while the groom was not exactly handsome, she was sure he would be very good to her. Besides, she said, she was glad to have had such a long and pleasant trip. Her only regret was that she now would probably never again see her father or mother. Perhaps, however, her brother would visit her new home in search of a wife for himself.

As Pedro and I proceeded, we looked back and saw that her kidnaper had placed the girl on the ground in front of his brother, who had knelt to feel her arms and legs and, possibly, to examine the teeth of his bride.

Like most rubber traders, Pedro Pablo was a poor man, but his home had an air of rustic magnificence. The clearing on which it was built had been hacked out of the jungle by machete, and the undergrowth was burned every year. It was surrounded on three sides by the cool green of the jungle and on the fourth by the lazy blue-brown of the Vaupés.

Pedro's own house included three spacious rooms and two smaller ones. It was the size of a large New York apartment. The one-story house was built on seven-foot poles, the floor and walls of pachuca palm bark, the roof of beautifully interlaced leaves of the caraña palm. On each side, in line with a wide open corridor which faced the jungle, was a roughhewn ladder. Next door on one side was a large mud hut in which lived the handful of Indians who part of the year helped cultivate the vegetables that were growing in the clearing. The rest of the time they gathered wild rubber. On the other side was a second mud hut in which a fire burned constantly. Here the cooking was done for Pedro's family and for the Indians.

Pedro's wife—legally I suppose she would be described as a common-law wife—was a chubby, soft-spoken Indian woman who was always smiling and whose eyes followed Pedro wherever he went. They had two laughing brown children who never bothered with clothes.

I spent four wonderfully restful days there, sleeping as many as twelve hours a night, in the daytime reading, making penciled notes concerning the expedition in the huge, lined high school notebooks I always carry with me, and watching the slow, unmeasured movement of the life around me.

I was not in a hurry. I never am on an expedition. Speed is impossible. Those who travel on a schedule should stay out of the South American jungles. Most tasks are put off not only until tomorrow but next week, next month, or, if at all possible, next year. Nothing much has changed in the last thousand years, and nothing much will change in the next thousand. That is why I like being there.

During the day I would hang my hammock on the open, porch-like corridor and, when I had tired of reading or note-taking, observe the Desano Indian women making *fariña* and *mañoco*. Both are prepared from yuca tubers, which contain prussic acid and, when eaten raw, are fatally poisonous. The acid is removed by making them into fariña and mañoco.

To make fariña, the women first soak the tubers in water for several days. Then they are peeled and mashed. Next the mash is poured into a long cylinder made of ribbons of palm leaves, which are squeezed to remove all the water. The remaining paste is then placed in an outdoor oven and stirred with a stick until completely dry. The result looks something like oatmeal.

Fariña is eaten with water; otherwise, not even the Desano stomach could hold it. Its taste is flat and somewhat rancid; I've tried it with sugar, with salt and pepper, and straight. It has always been completely indigestible for me; on the other hand, the natives seem to thrive on it.

Mañoco is prepared from the same yuca tubers, but, in this case, they are first peeled, at which point they look rather like lengthy, thin potatoes. Then they are grated on a special wooden board. After that, the mash is placed in a wonderfully practical sieve made of woven palm leaves; next the sieve is pounded with a stick. The liquid starch that emerges is caught in a container. Then the mash is put in the same palm cylinder or *tipiti* as is used for making fariña. Again the tipiti is squeezed to remove the liquid in the mash. Next the mash is once more taken to the open oven and patted into large, flat cakes resembling white pancakes, white that is, until the women rub their hands over their bodies

64

and pat their perspiration into the cake for flavoring. By this time the cakes usually take on an unappetizing grayish hue.

To get an idea of the taste, try dipping a large rubber eraser into glue; let the glue dry. Then try chewing the eraser.

Fortunately the Desanos also eat fish and whatever wild game they can kill plus a few wild fruits and roots, but, best of all, they cultivate the sweetest pineapples found anywhere in the world, including Hawaii.

They almost never have indigestion.

At least one part of Pedro's diet was even less appetizing. One morning shortly after breakfast he rushed into the house carrying a small, palm-leaf basket filled with what he assured me was a rare delicacy. At first I thought he had gathered some large black-brown berries. Then I looked again. The contents of the basket were moving. It was filled with live bacha ants, each with delicate gossamer-like wings about half an inch long.

Pedro tore the wings and legs off one and, after it had wriggled through his lips, chewed it thoroughly, then swallowed it.

Immediately his wife and children reached into the basket and grabbed handfuls of the crawling ants. The children stuffed two into their mouths at a time, smacking their lips with delight. Then, at Pedro's insistence, I tried one, but it gave me a vicious bite on the lower lip, and I spat it out.

One evening Pedro and a couple of Indians and I went on a paca hunt. The paca is a long, cumbersome rodent which looks, smells, and acts like its smaller brother, the rat. It emerges from its cave at night and wanders along the bank of the river looking for food. We would wait until one appeared, then shine a flashlight in its face, and, while it was temporarily blinded, shoot it. No skill is involved.

The sight of a skinned paca is likely to turn a delicate stomach.

65

At that point its resemblance to a dog-sized rat is alarmingly exact. However, I shut my eyes, and the next noon when Pedro's wife served me a paca steak I even asked for a second helping. The meat tastes like a stringy grade of beef.

One afternoon at Pedro's the heat was so oppressive I was unable to sleep during the siesta. Instead I decided to take a walk into the jungle. As I reached the edge of the clearing, I saw a completely nude Indian girl in her teens sitting in the jungle gloom on a pile of dry leaves. Her back was writhing, and I could see that she was occupied with some painful task.

I moved forward slowly, taking each step with care. When I reached a spot where I could see the girl clearly, I blanched. The girl held two equal lengths of strings made of tightly woven palm leaves. She had separated them in the middle and skillfully placed her pubic hair between the two strands. Then she brought the two strings together and gave a vicious jerk. Half her pubic hair was removed with one pull. She repeated the process, and again. Her face remained calm; it was as if she suffered no pain at all. After she had jerked a fourth and fifth time, not a hair remained. She paused for a moment, presumably to regain her strength.

As she did so, I stepped forward, and a branch crackled underfoot. The girl gave one terrified glance in my direction, screamed, and ran back into the clearing, toward the mud hut.

I was ashamed of what I had seen—but also puzzled. I thought perhaps the girl was demented, but later that afternoon when I questioned Pedro he simply shrugged. The male Indians of the Kubeo, Desano, and Guanano tribes dislike pubic hair on their women, he explained; they believe that the devil resides therein. As a result, the agonizing operation I had seen is by no means uncommon.

"For love," Pedro added philosophically, "women will do almost anything. Besides, here they do not cover their faces with paint."

Just before dawn the next morning Pedro, four Desanos, and I started down the Vaupés in a dugout, for the Macú country. By noon we had reached the lonely spot where the Abiyu flows into the Vaupés. The difference between the two rivers is immediately apparent. At this point the Vaupés has changed into a muddy brown and the Abiyu is an inky black.

The Abiyu is an evil river, the Desanos said, but they whispered the words. They did not wish to be heard by the monsters lurking everywhere.

I could believe them; the Abiyu does have a foreboding look. In addition to its gloomy blackness it is nowhere more than thirty yards across; it is always shallow; it has no banks; its waters carelessly flood into the jungle on either side, and twice that morning we came across fallen tree trunks which blocked the way. Both times we had to unload the dugout, pile our supplies in the nearest dry portion of the jungle, pick up the heavy batelo and carry it over the tree trunk, then reload. Our progress was exasperatingly slow.

However, by midafternoon Pedro sighed with relief; we were, he said, very near the Macú country now, and he pointed to the impressive man-made palisade just ahead. The river there was perhaps twenty yards across, and a fence of huge wooden stakes had been built from shore to shore. It was at least thirty feet above the water level. There was also a large, ingenious door in the palisade which, when lifted, was precisely the right size for the dugout to pass through.

This was where the Macues do their fishing. They gather

lengths of a thick, ropelike bush called *barbasco* and pound it into a milky pulp which is thrown into the water several yards up river from the palisade. A few minutes later the fish rise to the surface and float belly up to the palisade. They are not dead, but their respiratory organs have been temporarily paralyzed.

At that point the entire Macú community, from the oldest women to the youngest children, rushes into the water, some in dugouts, some on foot. Then they quickly gather up the fish, either with small nets or by hand. The operation does not last long, and, oddly enough, the barbasco pulp neither poisons the fish nor affects their taste. Those which are not picked up within a few minutes sometimes swim off again, apparently unharmed. Naturally no sport is involved, but the Macues do not fish for pleasure. They are an eternally hungry people.

After we passed the palisades, the Abiyu looked more like a swamp than a river; vegetation hung low on either side, and the water gradually became a dark, grayish red, a characteristic of many tributaries of the Vaupés. The waters of one small branch are so red that the Macues call it Tui, which means blood.

Toward dusk the river narrowed still more and at times was not much wider than the dugout. Twice again we had to unload the batelo and carry it over a huge, rotting palm trunk stretched from shore to shore. Our bodies dripped with perspiration, and the river was waist deep at that point. Once a *tirana* dropped on my soggy shirt from an overhanging branch. It lingered a moment, then flew off into the grayness. The tirana is a large bright green insect with huge wings. After mating the female eats the male, then searches for another victim.

Shortly after nightfall, wet, tired, hungry, and ill-tempered, we began to be attacked by ema ants, small reddish-brown creatures that travel in apparently well-disciplined armies, attacking every available portion of your body and with each bite injecting a tiny drop of fluid which burns for hours. They even get into your eyes, forcing out huge tears. Several times we had to jump into the river and completely submerge ourselves to get rid of them.

At around seven, since we knew the Macú settlement could not be far off, to save time, Pedro and I let the Desanos continue up the river with the dugout. We wearily trudged along the jungle path, brushing aside branches, watching carefully for snakes, which, by this time, had begun their nightly forage, occasionally dipping our arms and legs into the water to rid ourselves of the ants.

When we arrived after about forty-five minutes of walking, the Macú settlement was deserted. There were fires still burning in the maloca, plus the remains of half-eaten dinners, but the Macues were gone. They apparently had heard our footsteps and voices and were hiding in the jungle.

The silence was ominous. There was only the sluggish sound of the weary river, the leaves rustling in the jungle, and the occasional crackle of the cooking fires.

I immediately dropped to the ground.

"I don't care if I never see another Indian," I said. "I don't even care if the dugout doesn't show up. I'm going to sit right here, probably forever."

"Don't worry," said Pedro. "You will see plenty of Indians in a little while."

He paused. "I hope," he said, "that we haven't frightened them. A frightened Indian is a dangerous Indian."

I shrugged. At that particular moment nothing seemed to matter very much.

Three hours later the dugout arrived, but meantime so had the Macues.

69

Actually very little is known about the Macues. They are jungle nomads, apparently incapable of settling down. In most of the large area in the northwest of South America in which they are spread they are ferocious. They fight all strangers and resist any attempt at civilization. Around the Vaupés, however, they have long since been vanquished and made virtual slaves by the rest of the Tucano tribes. As a result they are completely servile. In many of the malocas of the Kubeo Indians I visited later there were nearly always a few Macues used for the meanest labor. They are given enough to eat and a sleeping space. They could escape or fight back, but, unlike most other tribes, they never do. They accept their demeaning fate without complaint.

The Macues in this particular area are not slaves, but they are not very belligerent, either.

The first we saw, a gnarled old man, wrinkled and bent, crept out of the jungle after about an hour. He was trembling visibly.

Pedro, who speaks the language, reached out his hand in a gesture of friendship, and, after hesitating a moment, the old man took it.

I was, Pedro explained, interested in becoming a friend of the Macues, and, to prove my sincerity, I had brought them many gifts.

The old man looked me over carefully, then nodded and went back to the forest to explain to the others. Most of them were out catching *tapura* worms, a staple of their diet.

The worms are thin, short, and white, and their capture involves one of the most elaborate and ingenious jungle operations I've ever witnessed. First, a fence made of smooth-surfaced *bijajio* is sewn together; the leaf is bent at the stem and falls to the ground at right angles when it is placed in a circle around a tree on which there is a horde of worms. Tiny holes are then dug by

70

hand at regular intervals inside the fence. Next the Macues shake the branches of the tree, and the worms fall to the ground, after which they crawl to the fence. Since they cannot escape, they begin circling the fence and fall into the holes. Then they are picked up and placed in hand-woven baskets. They are eaten roasted.

I spent eight lazy, luxurious days in the barnlike maloca of the Macues. It was seventy-five feet long and at least half that wide. The V-shaped roof was made of woven palm leaves supported by round, smooth tree trunks. Eight families lived inside. Each person had his own hammock, but there was just about as much privacy as in an army barracks.

I went on short treks into the jungle, slept a lot, and every morning and afternoon bathed in the Abiyu. The maloca was wisely located only two hundred yards from almost the only sandy beach along the entire length of the river.

One afternoon as I was about to jump into the water I heard a terrifying rattling sound directly behind me. I turned quickly and saw a huge *popumbo* spider on the sand a few inches from my feet. The popumbo is black and hairy, about the size of a man's hand, and belligerent. I grabbed the branch of a nearby tree and smashed it against a rock.

Some say the popumbo's bite is fatal; others disagree. I don't know. I do know that its favorite pastime is to jump on your bare feet and with its needle-sharp fangs inject a poison that at the very least is excruciatingly painful. At night it climbs down from its tree home and hunts for food, often killing and sucking the blood of small birds. Gustavo Rodríguez, a worldly friend of mine in Bogotá, once told me that he had caught five popumbos on his farm. He then took a needle and jabbed it into one of the spiders. When he removed the needle, only a stump was left. He tried the same experiment with a second spider; the result was the same.

Then he killed the other three spiders and stopped experimenting.

"There are some things I'd just as soon not know about," he said.

Like nearly all natives in the area of the Amazon, the Macues fornicate indiscriminately, get drunk whenever possible, and use narcotics. The narcotics are sometimes taken simply for intoxication, more often from habit, and usually just before a battle to work up artificial courage. The Macues, the women quite as much as the men, use coca mainly because they enjoy it and because it is so easy to prepare.

The leaves of the coca bush are first toasted in an open oven, then pounded into a powder in a wooden mortar about five feet deep. The depth is necessary to prevent the fine powder from diffusing into the air and choking the pounder. Finally the green powder is mixed with the ashes of yarumo leaves to give it a greater consistency.

Now it is ready for use. However, there is an art to taking coca. You pour the powder into your mouth with a small wooden dipper, being careful not to breathe until the powder has mixed with your saliva and formed a pasty ball which is kept in the inside of one cheek until it dissolves into the system. For several hours after that you feel that you are rich, handsome, charming, and indestructible.

However, I have never been able to share such a pleasant illusion because both times I tried taking coca I was unable to hold my breath long enough, and the powder went up both nostrils. I nearly choked to death.

The morning we left the Macues they all gathered around us, wearing the beads and carrying the mirrors I had given them,

silently and sadly watching our preparations for departure. Pedro
and I might be the last white men any of them would ever see.

The old man who had been the first to greet us solemnly shook
Pedro's hand, then mine.

"We wish you a speedy voyage and a quick return," he said. At
least that is what Pedro said he said. The others nodded their
agreement. Two young boys had earlier had to be ejected by force
from the dugout, which we had sent three and a half hours ahead
of us.

As Pedro and I started walking down the jungle path, two attractive, light-skinned girls, neither of whom could have been
more than thirteen, ran after us for almost half an hour.

When Pedro told them to go back, both shook their heads
vehemently and continued, always staying a few yards behind us.
Finally Pedro picked up a stick and shook it in their direction.
They stopped and for a moment looked as if they might be going
to cry—although Indians almost never do, in the presence of
white men anyway.

A few seconds later they turned and disappeared into the
jungle.

After they left Pedro smiled. "Perhaps I made a mistake," he
said. "On the dugout it sometimes becomes very cold at night."

It took us twice as long to go down river to the mouth of the
Abiyu as it had coming up. There had been no rain for a week,
and tree trunks and stumps which had been a foot below water
eight days before were now two feet above the surface. After we
met the dugout we often had to cut our way with axes and machetes. By that time the debris was too high for us to risk trying
to lift the batelo over it. Sometimes we stopped for an hour, hacking and chopping, before we were able to go ahead.

Once when we were passing under a particularly heavy growth

of branches, I looked up and saw two mating black scorpions hanging no more than an inch above our heads.

I yelled a warning but was too late. As the Desano in front of the dugout jerked backward, both scorpions dropped on him. He screamed and jumped into the water, nearly upsetting the heavily laden dugout.

When he came up for air, we could see that he had not been stung, but for the rest of the trip he talked about nothing else. The black scorpion's sting causes blood to flow from the pores of the skin, the eyes, the ears, and the nails. It is often fatal and is feared by the Indians even more than a snakebite.

The best remedies, Pedro explained, are to eat as much salt as possible, or to climb a tree or any other high place off the ground.

We also saw a great many snakes along the way, particularly *riecas*, or bushmasters, the largest of the poisonous snakes. The rieca's tail ends in what looks like a nail which digs into the ground when the snake is ready to strike. I've seen bushmasters ten to eleven feet long, and Pedro claimed to have killed one fifteen feet in length.

One of the Desanos, an otherwise muscular young man, had one foreleg which was as thin as a stick, the result of a rieca bite. He had recovered by drinking the sap made by pounding the roots of a plant called the *platanillo*. A dose about the size of a demitasse is required. However, if you drink the sap without having been bitten, you die—painlessly and instantly.

On every trip I take several vials of the two kinds of anti-snake serum prepared by the Butantan Institute of Brazil, one as protection against rattlers, the other for possible bites by members of the bothrop family. The bite of the South American rattler affects the nervous and respiratory systems; that of the bothrops, for example, the bushmaster, attacks the red corpuscles.

Once in a village on the Putumayo River I treated an Indian who six hours before had been bitten by a *taya*, one of the bothrop group. Blood gushed from every pore in his body, and he was already near death when I gave him twenty cubic centimeters of serum. An hour and a half later he had recovered completely and was so grateful that he tried to give me as a gift his twelve-year-old daughter.

When we reached the mouth of the Abiyu and passed into the waters of the Vaupés, it was nearly midnight. There was a full moon; a warming breeze wafted out from the jungle, and at that moment the Vaupés seemed as wide and as deep as the Mississippi. We heard the friendly howl of a monkey, and a parrot somewhere on shore was shouting something to a mate. The Desanos began laughing at some private joke, poking each other like delighted children.

Pedro lay down on the bottom of the boat and was instantly asleep. An hour later as we approached his house he awakened, sat up, and smiled. On shore we could see a group of huddled Desanos; they shouted greetings to our paddlers. Nearby were the dark outlines of Pedro's wife and his two children, waving vehemently.

For a moment Pedro was silent, but his lips moved noiselessly. Then he said, "Thank God we are back in civilization once more."

As soon as we had moored the boat Señora Pablo fixed us a delicious supper, and I retired to my hammock. I slept for more than twelve hours, which was just as well because the next night a *cachirí* had been planned in honor of our return at the Indian village of Tipiaca, a few miles down the river.

For days, Pedro said, the tubers of yuca had been fermenting, and the drink which resulted would, as he put it, "produce much drunkenness."

"The cachirí will be wild," he said. "You will have never seen anything like it."

I never have seen anything even remotely like it—with the possible exception of a New Year's Eve party at a country club in Fairfield County, Connecticut.

3

Whoever chose the site for Tipiaca had an eye for beauty. Its eight huts are built on a promontory overlooking one of the largest and surely most magnificent rapids along the entire Vaupés. The other three sides of the village are curtained with green.

Then there is the main maloca, a good seventy feet long and forty-five feet wide. From a height of thirty-five feet in the middle the V-shaped palm-leaf roof slopes at a forty-five-degree angle to within thirty inches of the ground. There is an entrance at either end, one for men, the other for women, though both sexes usually use both. During the day the palm curtains over the doors are pulled up and secured by a pole.

The roof is supported by round, tall tree trunks strategically spaced so that in the center is an unobstructed space about the size of a small ballroom. Here the dances and festivals are held. The women do their cooking in the rear, and the front is a combined reception room and burial ground. The chief is considered the owner of the maloca, and as soon as he is buried the building is abandoned and a new site chosen. The inhabitants of the maloca store their property—all of which, except for a few per-

76

sonal odds and ends, is communally owned—on shelves and roughly built stands on every side and along the frame of the roof. The graves sprinkled in the front part of the maloca are unmarked.

When a Desano dies, his body is wrapped in his hammock. Then his dugout is chopped into two pieces. His body is tenderly laid in one half; the other half is folded over as a cover. With him are placed his favorite headdress, his most colorful feather adornments, his best-loved trinkets, and enough food to sustain him during the long river journey on which he is about to embark— destination unknown. Next, a male friend blows tobacco smoke through both ends of the coffin, apparently in the belief that the smoke has some preservative quality. Then the chopped-up dugout is horizontally lowered into a deep hole in the front area of the maloca. After that the grave is carefully covered over. That is all. No words said, no wailing done. The weeping, if any, is a strictly private matter—just then anyway.

If, however, the death has resulted from illness, the friends and relatives frequently decide that the cause is some fellow inhabitant of the maloca who, possibly years before, has expressed a critical opinion of the deceased. The critic is immediately poisoned lest by some secret incantation he (or she) cause further deaths. Women are more often found guilty than men.

On the first anniversary of the death the funeral takes place.

The inside of the maloca is divided into two equal sections by a fence made of stems of *pari* palm; the mourners put on masks and ornaments made of bark cloth; the doors are closed, and the men remain in the front, the women in the rear. At that point, on a signal from the chief, the weeping and wailing begin on both sides of the fence. For two days and nights there is continuous shouting, screaming, singing, dancing, and drinking.

77

At dawn of the third day the ghost of the deceased unobtrusively creeps out of the maloca—possibly in search of peace and quiet. After that, life goes on as before.

In other parts of the Vaupés the body of the deceased is exposed to the open air and the birds and beasts until nothing remains but the skeleton. The process never takes long. Next the bones are ground into a white powder and mixed with cachirí. Then the relatives and closest friends of the deceased drink the concoction, I'm told, with the idea that it is better to be inside a friend than a snake or a jaguar.

By comparison the Desanos are a highly civilized people.

On my arrival in Tipiaca I hung my hammock in a tiny abandoned grass hut away from and a little above the rest of the village. From there I could see for several hundred yards up and down the river; the air was cooler and considerably fresher than below, and every night I was lulled to sleep by the muffled roar of the rapids.

I had expected to find some quiet there, too, but I never succeeded. I was immediately surrounded by curious children and women who unpacked all of my gear and exclaimed over each item.

Finally I inflated the small rubber raft I carry with me, and the curumis, as the children are called, ran happily down to the river to test it, followed by the shouting women.

A few minutes later I received a visit from the chief, a husky middle-aged man who smiled cautiously at me, then sat down on my hammock.

The position of chief is not hereditary among the Desanos; he is chosen because he is the bravest man of the maloca, the strongest, and, presumably, the wisest.

Pedro Pablo introduced us, and the chief, with Pedro translating, proceeded to put me through an interrogation as thorough as that of any of the U. S. Army intelligence officers who questioned me during the war. He wanted to know where I was born, how old I was, where I had traveled, what I thought of the Kubeos, the Macues, and his own people, what I was doing on the Vaupés, how long I planned to stay, and what I hoped to see. Apparently he considered me reliable, because a few minutes later he nodded, rose, and motioned for Pedro and me to follow him down to a deserted spot on the banks of the river several hundred yards below the settlement proper. Here, he said, pointing to an almost undiscernible mound of earth, was where the Yuruparí was buried.

Then he explained. The Desanos worship a kind of devil-god, also called the Yurupari. Twice a year the festival of the Yurupari is celebrated. Everybody becomes demonstrably drunk, both men and women. Then the men go to the riverbank and dig up the Yurupari, eight wooden flutes varying in size from one to four feet.

As soon as the older men start playing the flutes, the unmarried women, hearing the painfully eerie sound, flee into the jungle.

Then the payé, or witch doctor, appears, wearing an enormous bark cloth mask on which the grotesque approximations of human features have been painted. The payé does a weird dance more or less in tune with the flutes.

Next, the boys who have arrived at puberty since the last festival jump into the river and bathe near the spot where the flutes have been hidden.

After that the whole male population, led by the writhing payé, returns to the maloca. There the boys being initiated into the tribe are flogged with special sticks and whips with several strands of vine at one end; the beating continues until their bodies are a bloody mass of welts and bruises, after which the older men lash each other to prove their fortitude. No one ever displays any emotion. By that time most of them are so intoxicated that they are, I imagine, incapable of feeling pain.

Then the Yuruparí flutes are once more returned to the riverbank and buried.

Finally the unmarried women of the tribe are called in from the jungle, given a little cachirí, and beaten until they too are covered with bruises and blood. They do not complain; the women are accustomed to rough treatment. They are all expected to be faithful to their husbands—except during a cachirí, when they can retire to the bushes with anybody they choose or with as many men as they wish. However, an unmarried woman who becomes pregnant is treated as a prostitute until, by taking an herb concoction mixed by the payé, she gets rid of the unborn child.

Among the Desanos, if a woman does not bear children for her husband, he takes a second wife and, if necessary, a third. All of the wives are expected to and usually do live amicably together. Separations are almost non-existent.

Usually a Yuruparí festival ends without tragedy—except for a few dozen bruised and bleeding bodies. However, should an unmarried girl be unlucky enough to run in the wrong direction when she hears the wooden flutes and, by some mischance, see the flutes, she is immediately put to death by poisoning.

Several years ago two Catholic missionaries in the region of the Vaupés decided to end, once and for all, this macabre custom. They somehow got hold of the sacred flutes, called all the unmarried girls together, and held up the Yuruparí. The girls fled in panic, but it was too late. The payé decided that one out of ten had to be killed, and they were. After explaining the Yuruparí festival to Pedro and me the chief led us back to the village and introduced us to the youthful payé.

The payé was a crafty-looking young man who disliked me on sight. He made me think of a naked, darker version of Merlin in Mark Twain's *A Connecticut Yankee in King Arthur's Court*. His gestures were exaggerated, his speech loud, slow, and deliberate. He was a born ham who had been trained for his job since birth.

Moreover he had been put through a series of painful tests by other payés. During the initiation ceremony he had had to inhale a series of resins in powder form; palm needles had been stuck all over his chest and forearms; bird feathers had been forced up his nostrils, and he had had to remain silent. If he had displayed either pain or emotion, he would have found himself unemployed.

He has to sing tribal chants, and volume is more important than voice quality. He must be able to bring on sunshine when that is needed, an eclipse when one seems desirable. He must know how to kill by sorcery, locate lost objects, predict the time and place of enemy attack, insure victory, and, most important of all, produce an instantaneous thunderstorm when one is necessary for the crops or when his chief feels one would make a pleasant break in the monotony of life in the maloca. This last is not really very difficult in a place where it rains almost continuously for months on end and where thunder is an inevitable accompaniment.

In addition the payé is expected to foretell the future and to remember the past. If a major prediction fails or his memory proves faulty, he is immediately put to death. If a member of the maloca is attacked by a jaguar, the payé is given a quick-working poison.

If one of his sick patients dies, the payé is killed.

81

However, throughout his frequently short life he is looked upon as a kind of god on earth, particularly in case of sickness. Half the time his treatment consists of nothing more than a series of loud shouts and the wearing of a supposedly frightening mask. Nevertheless, in those tribes that have contact with the white man, if a native asks for medical treatment, it is mainly out of curiosity. He prefers the more familiar methods of his local payé.

Sometimes, as men will, he dies for his stupidity, too. For instance, for a serious cold, a common ailment among Indians, the patient is usually thrown in the river. If he is unable to rise from his hammock, he is doused with cold water. Pneumonia and death often result. Of course, the payé doesn't survive either.

But since the smart payé depends quite as much on the use of herbs as on chants, he often meets with success. On one expedition I had a serious ear infection. Before leaving Bogotá I had already had ninety-seven shots of sulfa and penicillin. Still the infection remained. When I mentioned it to the local payé he poured some kind of herb liquid into my ear. In forty-eight hours the infection had disappeared, and I haven't been bothered since.

When I awoke on my first morning in Tipiaca, an exquisite-looking girl of perhaps fifteen was standing just inside the door of my hut, looking down at me. However, as soon as I opened my eyes, she ran. That afternoon I took my usual walk in the jungle; after about half an hour I heard gentle footsteps behind me; I half turned, and the same girl disappeared in the dimness.

Her name was Yosefá.

Toward evening, while I was writing in one of my notebooks, I felt someone staring at me through a crack in the wall. It was Yosefá again. I rose, but by the time I reached the door of the hut, she was halfway down the hill.

She was a tall, light-skinned girl, almost perfectly proportioned. Her high cheekbones were delicately molded, her half-slanting eyes a startling black, her mouth wide and generous, her teeth, as is true of almost all Desanos, beautifully white.

However, when I saw her that night in the maloca, she seemed unaware of my presence. I realized that since many white traders had passed through the area she had been told that all white men are dangerous. Sometimes when a trader is visiting a native settlement, an Indian girl will climb into his hammock without an invitation after he retires. More often, however, he simply chooses the one he prefers and forces her to sleep with him. The men of the maloca will not usually attack him, but they normally punish the girl after he is gone. In a few cases she is even put to death.

Naturally Yosefá was afraid of me. The next morning, when she peered into my hut, I took a pair of huge red earrings from my gear and extended them toward her. Again she ran, but a few minutes later she was back. By that time I had placed the earrings on the ground in the middle of the hut. She motioned for me to step away from them, which I did. Then she darted into the hut, grabbed them, and a moment later was down at the river, examining herself in the placid waters.

During my jungle walk that afternoon, I again came across Yosefá. This time she was returning to the maloca, carrying a basket filled with yuca tubers. When she saw me she dropped the basket and ran, but was back in a second or two, this time following me. I did my best to show that my intentions were friendly, but she was unconvinced.

As I walked toward her she dashed behind a tree. I reached for her, and as I did so she pushed my hand against the tree trunk. I howled with pain. When I withdrew my hand Yosefá was gone, but my hand was covered with thorns half an inch long.

When I sat down to begin the painful task of removing them, her raucous laughter echoed through the jungle.

My hand burned for days, and for the rest of my stay in Tipiaca I treated Yosefá with friendly respect.

The day of the cachirí was hot; the sun beat down relentlessly; clouds of steam arose from the jungle, and there was not even the suggestion of a breeze. I spent most of the morning by the river-bank, making believe that the roar of the rapids made the air cooler, knowing that it did not.

When, shortly after noon, I slowly sauntered up the hill to the maloca, I saw that the entrance was crowded with pushing, gig-gling natives. They were like fretful children on Christmas Eve. The cachirí, the name given both to the celebration and to the highly intoxicating drink made from yuca tubers, was about to begin.

In an otherwise hopelessly drab life the cachirí is always a highly successful diversion. It rarely lasts less than two or three days and nights and has been known to go on for a week or more. Several additional days are required to recover from the hangover.

Any excuse will do—an exchange of presents between neighbor-ing tribes, a victory, or, as in this case, a visitor. Besides, it is al-ways possible for the payé or the chief to invent the reason for a cachirí.

Inside the maloca both the men and the women were dressing for the party. First, the women were painting each other and then the men with red *achote* dye, made from the pit of a small peach-like fruit, as well as a black dye. Horizontal, vertical, and slanting lines were drawn on everyone's arms, legs, face, and body. The designs were similar; yet each differed slightly.

In addition the men fastened strings of the stones of fruit and

84

fish and animal bones around their legs. On their heads they wore the most elaborate feather headdresses, again each differing and each a work of art. By contrast the women seemed curiously drab. Their only decorations were the painted red lines.

By sunset hundreds of guests had arrived, some by dugout, others on foot. They had come from just over the hill, from miles up and down the river, from deep inside the jungle. The news that free liquor is available gets around just as quickly as anywhere else. Altogether there were about three hundred celebrants in Tipiaca that night.

A few days earlier the nearby neighbors had arrived with bowls of cachirí. These, in addition to the tuber pulp and water fermented in Tipiaca itself, were poured into large hollow tree trunks and left. Shortly after dusk the liquor was dipped into huge bowls and carried inside the maloca. Flaming torches of slow-burning turi palm wood were placed at strategic intervals around the walls.

There was a moment of awed silence. Then the men gathered in front of the maloca, and the women seated themselves along the sides and in the back. Bowls of cachirí were passed, and after everyone had drunk enough to relax sufficiently eight young men with magnificent physiques lined up in front of the chief. He spoke a few quick words to them, and they replied in unison, at the same time rhythmically moving from side to side the flute each held in his right hand. They paused; the leader gave a sharp command and the eight men made a circle around the cleared space in the center. Next each placed his left hand on the shoulder of the next dancer, meantime repeating the same four or five monotonous notes on his flute. They took two short steps, then a long step, two shorts and a long. In a few minutes a group of women cut into the chain, again two short steps, one long one.

On each side smaller circles were formed, the men playing larger, louder, but equally monotonous-sounding flutes. There, too, the steps never varied. They never did.

Every once in a while someone would drop out, grab the nearest bowl, and take deep swallows, then dart back into the dance. Once a long, conga-like line was formed; again there were a dozen small circles through the maloca, some moving clockwise, some counterclockwise. The flutes droned on, and there was the sound of the strings of bone and snake rattlers rubbing together. The painted snake bodies glistened with perspiration; clouds of dust rose from the dry earth, and the air inside soon became oppressive. After a few moments I rose from my seat, a huge, throne-like wooden chair belonging to the chief, and went outside to breathe the cool night air.

When I returned a group of older men had squatted on the ground in two equal rows facing each other. They shouted indistinguishable words at each other, meantime passing a huge cigar from man to man. Each would take a puff, blow a mouthful of smoke at the man across from him, then pass the cigar to his neighbor.

As I watched, the dancers became fewer in number. A man and a woman, almost never a husband and wife, would leave the dance floor hand in hand and return perhaps half an hour later; a little while after that each would choose another partner and leave for a second time, and a third, on and on throughout the night. There was considerable competition for the virgins, usually girls who had not yet reached their teens, but who gave themselves drunkenly, willingly, and often.

When a girl reaches puberty, her hair is cut short, her face painted red, and she is sent into seclusion in the jungle for several days. She is said to lose her virginity to the moon while there, but no one believes such nonsense. If the girl has not already been deflowered at a cachirí—which is usually the case—an old man does it with his finger. Women who are menstruating are forced to live in a special hut built for that purpose in the jungle. If they stayed in the maloca and some calamity occurred while they were there, such as an illness, it would be necessary to poison the menstruating women. Intercourse almost never takes place inside the maloca. If it did, the child would be born lazy.

By dawn, when I started to my hut to get some sleep, a few dancers were still upright, but the flames had burned out and the supply of cachirí was nearly exhausted.

As I walked up the hill the path on either side was littered with dusty, paint-smeared bodies of unconscious men and women.

I had planned a short expedition for the next day. I wanted to climb Muj-Tuke, a two-pronged rock hill a few miles from Tipiaca. The hill towered at least fifteen hundred feet above the jungle, and the Indians said only the lower prong had been scaled, but I hoped to find a way to the summit of the higher one.

However, I had to wait. It was three days before the chief and the old man who had volunteered to accompany me had recovered from the cachirí.

The three of us left Tipiaca at dawn of the fourth day, and after two hours of hacking our way through the tangled underbrush we reached the base of Muj-Tuke. At first any ascent seemed impossible. The sides were smooth and round; there did not seem to be a single protuberance at any height. However, by hanging onto the profuse vines and roots which were everywhere we managed to work our tortuous way up the slippery boulders which at times sloped down at a forty-degree angle and at others were almost vertical.

Several times we were attacked by hordes of emá ants but

finally, after what seemed hours, we reached the opening of a narrow, dark corridor. On one side was a sheer thousand-foot precipice fenced off on one side by two ancient trees, on the other a shorter, sloping rock. We crawled through the corridor on our hands and knees and at the end came to the foot of the higher of the two prongs.

It was a round, barren rock pointing like a giant finger into the sky. From where we stood we could not even see the top of the peak. I realized then that it would be impossible to scale, and I was sick with disappointment.

However, as we turned and looked below, I gasped with delight. Below on every side stretched the green sea of jungle, the pattern broken only by the shadow of an occasional cloud. To the east was a narrow blue range of mountains, and to the west the comforting, lazy smoke of the cooking fires of Tipiaca. We stood in hushed silence for a moment. Then the chief spoke, and the old man translated his words.

He said something like this: "Many men have suffered much trying to climb this mountain. I now understand why."

I agreed.

The descent was fearful. We slid down with our bodies close to the rock to create more friction, thus slowing us down. A false step anywhere would have meant a fall of at least a thousand feet. Several times we held hands, first lowering the old man down the perpendicular wall until he reached another ledge and was able to grab onto a vine; the chief went next, and I was last.

By the time we reached the foot of the cliff we were exhausted; our bodies were masses of emá bites, and we hurried to a nearby creek and bathed in the cool, refreshing water. Two hours later we were back in Tipiaca, and I was back on my hammock. I slept until midafternoon of the next day.

The following afternoon Pedro and I started back up the Vaupés to his home. After a couple of days there we began the trip back to Mitú, spending our nights at the lonely, barren huts of the rubber traders, who, without exception, were delighted at our arrival and heartbroken when we departed.

The first night we didn't sleep at all. Our host was a chunky, garrulous man with soft, poetic eyes, a handle-bar mustache, and a tongue that never stopped wagging. His tiny two-room hut was lined with well-thumbed books of all kinds, and after supper he dragged out a bottle and started talking.

By breakfast time we had finished the bottle, but Señor Linares, who considered himself the best and possibly the only philosopher of the Vaupés, had still not delivered himself of all of his opinions. His main preoccupation was with the demented condition of the entire human race, possibly, he admitted, including himself.

"There isn't a sane man on this earth," he said at one point, gesturing emphatically with the half-full glass in his hand. "We are all crazy in some sort of way, and madness is relative to the capacity to understand it.

"Take, for example, the two nuts confined in an asylum. They saw a stream of water coming out of a pipe. One tried to cut the stream with a machete; the other attempted to tie together the two ends thus obtained.

"After twenty-five years of this game one said to the other, 'Just think if we did not have this diversion, we would probably be crazy.'"

Señor Linares chortled with delight.

"But you," he went on, shaking his fat finger in my face, "you are the craziest of all. A sane man would travel along this Godforsaken river only through necessity. You do it because you choose to do so. You are thoroughly mad.

"However," he concluded, "you will not live long."

And he laughed again.

As his sad eyes followed us up the river, I realized that Señor Linares would probably not see another white man for six months, perhaps longer, and I wondered if, perhaps, he wasn't right after all. In his own case anyway.

Back in Mitú, Señor Cayzedo and the chief of police were still sitting at the same paper-littered table on the same second floor of the comisaría. Between them was what was another bottle of aguardiente.

When I walked in, three mouths dropped open, and Señor Cayzedo looked first at me, then at Pedro.

He closed his mouth, called for two more glasses, filled them, and said, "Frankly, I never expected to see you again, but I am glad you have returned. Drink up."

We did.

"And how were the Macues?" the chief wanted to know. "How did they look?"

I said that the Macues looked very much like any other Indians.

The chief nodded. "You see," he said, smiling, "I told you as much these many weeks ago. You could have seen Indians on the streets of Mitú. Yet you trek down a river and through the jungles to see more Indians." He shrugged.

"You should drink more aguardiente," he said. "Then you would realize when you are well off."

I nodded, and I had another drink of aguardiente. The next morning, with a hangover, I boarded the plane for Bogotá, and eight days later was on my way to Boston, Massachusetts.

A couple of weeks after the term opened one of my professors asked me how I'd spent the summer. Remembering Señor Linares and the chief of police in Mitú, I said I had spent a very quiet summer in Bogotá.

"You must be crazy," said the professor, who was an amateur anthropologist. "If I were a young man and had all that unexplored jungle at my back door, not to mention those fascinating and largely unknown Indian tribes, I'd spend my summers finding out something about them."

He walked down the hall shaking his head sadly.

4

The girl sitting on the rough wooden bench was wearing a dress of the brightest yellow, and this was all she was wearing. It took only a glance to determine that.

As I entered the cluttered, unswept little store, the man standing behind her looked up at me and frowned. He had just made a joke, and the girl leaned against him and laughed.

I took a second, closer look at her, and then, as I had when I first saw her on the Meta five years before, I gasped.

The girl was Catani.

When I caught her eye, her face blanched, and she started to speak, then changed her mind. The recognition had been instantaneous on her part too.

At nineteen Catani was no longer a child. Her sleek black hair was longer now, and it was gathered into a loose roll at the nape of her neck. Her dark brown eyes were more placid, but there was a look of determination in them. Both her face and her body had rounded into maturity, and her legs, which dangled over the counter, were perfectly formed. As before, the dress was too tight and was far too short, but now I had the feeling that she knew what it did for her and had chosen it for that reason. She was still barefoot.

She sat there for a moment, perfectly still. The man behind the counter cleared his throat noisily. Then Catani jumped down from the counter and ran toward the door. Her shoulder brushed mine as she passed.

I realized that from the intimate way Catani had been leaning against him that her relationship with the man behind the counter was by no mean casual. Naturally I examined him closely.

He was young, in his mid-thirties, I imagine, and in a rough way he might have been considered handsome. He was a little less than six feet tall, thin, and muscular. He wore long, narrow sideburns, had a neatly trimmed mustache over his thin lips, and his active dark eyes were separated by a nose shaped like an eagle's beak. It was apparent from the first that he hated and possibly even feared me.

"I'd like some rice and salt," I said, keeping my voice calm.

The man shrugged. "Help yourself," he said.

As I selected my supplies from his meager stock, I avoided looking at the storekeeper again, but after I had paid him I smiled and, making it sound as casual as possible, I said, "That girl who was just in here looked very familiar. I wonder if I could possibly have seen her before."

The man silently counted out my change.

"I have a feeling," I went on, "that she's the same girl I saw several years ago on the Meta."

Still no answer.

"I'm not sure," I said, "but I seem to remember that that girl was named"—I hesitated—"something like Catani."

The man frowned. "That's Catani, all right," he said curtly.

I gathered up my purchases and started toward the door. "That's what I thought," I said as if her identity had been a matter of no importance to me.

The storekeeper grunted.

I had stopped at the tiny settlement on my way to Caucayá, where I was getting a Catalina plane back to Bogotá. It was late summer, the year after my graduation from M.I.T., and I was on my way back from a thousand-mile expedition, partly by jungle trail and partly by boat, up the Putumayo River. I had been gone for a little more than eight weeks.

Like most stopovers of its kind, this outpost had only about ten houses and one large and several small stores. I was spending the night with my four Huitoto Indian guides in the home of Señor José Villas, a middle-aged Brazilian trader.

On my way to his place a good-looking young Indian who must have been about Catani's age stopped me.

"Do you remember me?" he asked, smiling.

I looked him over and said no, I didn't.

"I saw you about five years ago on the Meta," he said. "You'd just finished a trip across the llanos."

He paused. "I recognized you from the green hat," he said.

I'd bought my cork hat in Bogotá just before taking off on my first expedition. It was an ordinary enough sun helmet until I painted it green, mostly, I rationalized, to preserve it, but more, I am sure, because, like almost everyone else, I like to be recognized. Painted green, the helmet was probably the only one of its kind in all of Amazonia.

"You must be a Guahibo," I told the young Indian. "What are you doing this far from the Meta?"

"That," he said, looking unhappy, "is a long story, but I want

93

to go back now. I thought you might take me along if you're going in that direction."

I could use another paddler, so I told him I would give him a lift as far as Caucayá. He promised to be ready to leave at dawn the next morning.

"I must first say my farewells to Catani," he said, turning.

For the rest of the night his words stayed with me.

In addition to myself and the five Huitotos, Señor Villas had a sixth guest that night, a Catholic missionary who, since he is typical of so many hundred representatives of the Church in the area of the Amazon, need not be named. He was a short, squat man, his face burned black by the sun; he had a gentle smile, a sense of good-natured mischief in his darting brown eyes, and the air of a man who, despite months of isolation in the jungle, enjoyed life and made the most of it.

That night over a bottle of wine he examined my photographic equipment with admiration, then showed me his own Rolleiflex, which he had recently bought in Manáos, the now-disintegrating onetime capital of the rubber-gathering area of the Putumayo, about which I'll have a good deal to say later.

"I got $200 for my old camera," said the father, his eyes crinkling with delight, "which is quite a feat since it originally had cost only $100, and that was six years ago.

"To accomplish so remarkable an achievement, I conducted a raffle at one of the larger Indian villages on the way to Manáos. I sold four hundred tickets at fifty cents each. Thus, the Indian who won it received a $100 camera for only fifty cents."

He paused, then, "Can you tell me anyplace else in the world where one could obtain so cheap a camera?"

He laughed and slapped his knee.

94

"I should have become a businessman instead of a missionary," he said. "I would easily have become a millionaire."

He poured himself another glass of wine.

There was a moment of silence inside Señor Villas' tiny house, interrupted only by the heavy, regular breathing of the four Indians, who had already retired to their hammocks. Outside a woman screamed, but no one paid any attention.

A few minutes later Señor Villas took another puff from the huge brier pipe he smoked and began a story he had, I was sure, told many times before and which, like the excellent wine he was serving us, had improved with age.

"It was many years ago," he began. "I was young then, much thinner, and eager for adventure.

"I was also unafraid of life or death or failure; now I fear all three."

He laid the still-smoking pipe on the table beside him.

"There were four of us," he went on, "none more than twenty-five, and we had gone up a tributary of the Río Negro to look for rubber forests. Each of us then dreamed," and he sighed, "that he would be the one to find a new and untouched forest and would become rich and powerful and thus be able to escape from the jungle.

"We were all four wrong." He took up his pipe again.

"However, on this occasion we late one afternoon heard an ominous rumbling noise in the jungle, and we walked away from the river to discover its origin. One of my companions said the noise might have been made by a group of Macues, and we laughed at him. We assured him that what we had heard was only an animal.

"We had not gone more than five hundred yards when, without warning, the dart from a blowgun struck one of my com-

95

panions—the one who had suggested the possibility of Indians—in the neck. Instantly a screaming group of Macues emerged from behind trees and began rushing toward us.

"There was a moment of confusion, then three of us turned and ran back toward the river. Our courage had disappeared at the sight of the first Indian; so had our sense of decency. We left the wounded man lying on the ground behind us.

"When we reached the river, we plunged in and started across. Our dugout was too far downstream even to think of reaching it in time to save our own necks.

"Fortunately we crossed without difficulty.

"However, just before the last of our trio reached the far bank he was bitten by a piranha. As so rarely happens, he was able to step onshore before he was attacked by the thousands of other piranhas who had simply been waiting for the first drop of blood.

"He dropped on the bank of the river, terrified and exhausted.

"Myself and my remaining unwounded companion dragged him behind a cluster of trees a few feet away, then we took our guns and aimed for the still-screaming Macues, who had plunged into the water after us.

"Two shots were sufficient. In a few seconds the water was tinted with blood, and after that the piranhas took over.

"Of the twenty Macues in the group pursuing us only four were able to retreat to the opposite bank, and these were bleeding profusely. A few minutes later two were no longer writhing with pain.

"As for the sixteen who were unable to escape, they screamed with terror for several minutes. Then all was quiet, and there was only the rapidly expanding pool of bloody water to remind us that they had ever existed. The two who survived had already crawled back into the jungle.

"By this time my friend who had been bitten by the first piranha had recovered sufficiently to accompany us down river to the spot where we had left the dugout. We then made a raft of logs, crossed to the other side, and in a few minutes found the man who had been hit by the dart of the blowgun.

"He was already dead of the poison, and we knew from the look in his bulging eyes that it had not been an easy death. We lifted his body into the dugout, and the next morning quietly buried him along the banks of the river.

"Naturally there was no priest available, Father; so I said a few inadequate words over his unmarked grave, and then we returned to our homes.

"I think that was the experience which convinced me that I would never escape the jungle."

His pipe had gone out, and Señor Villas relighted it. Then he smiled.

"Of course," he said, "I have more cheerful stories, but not tonight. It is late."

It was I who broke the silence which followed. I had to ask about Catani.

Señor Villas smiled indulgently. "On those rare occasions when I have visitors from the outside," he said, "I make bets with myself. Since her arrival there has not been a visitor to this settlement who has not inquired about her or who, for that matter, has not dreamed of taking her with him.

"I wager with myself whether the first question about her will be before, during, or after dinner. Usually it is before. You have shown remarkable restraint, Señor Acebes."

He knocked the tobacco from his pipe.

"I must warn you," he said. "That girl is trouble, serious trouble."

I nodded. "I know," I said, "and my interest in her is impersonal." (I was sorry to be lying). "I met her on the Meta five years ago, and I was wondering how she got this far down." The distance was approximately one thousand miles.

"Of that," said Señor Villas, "I am not certain. All I know is that she arrived here about eight months ago with Joaquín, the storekeeper, and an Indian boy. Although he is a friend of mine, Joaquín has never even mentioned her name to me. I am curious, but I know when to keep my own counsel. A few weeks ago he knocked a man to the floor for doing no more than ask her name. As the man got up, Joaquín threatened to rip open his stomach if he said another word about her.

"Ten minutes later the man was on his way down the river."

Señor Villas poured himself another glass of wine and, carefully avoiding the eye of the missionary, he said, "I need hardly add that she and Joaquín are sharing a hammock."

The missionary shrugged. "Such things happen," he said, "particularly among the semicivilized. It is only among certain tribes of uncivilized Indians that constancy is observed in this region.

"However," he went on, "women like this Catani have the devil in them, and men should beware when they go near them."

"Perhaps," I said, smiling, "that is the reason men are unable to stay away from them."

"Well, she certainly is an unusual woman," Señor Villas added hurriedly. "Very unusual. Fortunately for my own peace of mind I am now too old to be interested—except, as you put it, Señor Acebes, in an impersonal way."

The missionary rose and patted my shoulder. "I am glad you are leaving tomorrow, my boy," he said, "because I can see that you have Castilian blood in your veins."

He winked. "And now I am going to sleep."

98

I, too, retired a few minutes later, but I was unable to sleep. My mind was filled with the vision of Catani in the tight yellow dress, and the fear and, I liked to think, the interest in her eyes when she saw me for the second time in five years. I also kept thinking of the handsome young Indian boy who had come with her from the Meta and of Joaquín, the storekeeper.

The next morning I had dark circles under my eyes.

Although it was only a little after seven, the sun was already high in the sky, and as my four Huitoto guides and I crawled into the dugout, the young Guahibo appeared over a nearby hill. His only belongings were wrapped in a corner of his hammock, which he carried over his back.

A few feet behind him came Catani. She looked sleepy, and her eyes were red, as if she had been crying, but she was still beautiful. She was wearing the same yellow dress as the day before. Her eyes were on the Guahibo, and she seemed to be unaware of my presence.

I dangled my feet over the sides of the dugout, ostentatiously blowing cigar smoke out of my mouth.

The Guahibo threw his hammock into the boat, then turned, nodded curtly, and said a single word. It was the Guahibo equivalent of good-by. After that he climbed into the dugout, picked up a long pole, and with the help of the Huitotos started pushing the boat away from shore.

Catani did not speak, but as the boat started down the river she turned, her shoulders shaking. Then she drew herself up, and, just before we rounded a bend in the river, began waving. The Guahibo did not wave back. To have done so would have been unmanly.

I was cautious in my approach to him. For two days and two nights I said nothing about Catani. I perspired in the sun; I shivered in the rain; I watched the monotonous life of the jungle on both banks of the river; I smoked cigars; occasionally I read a little or helped paddle the dugout; I slept.

On the morning of the third day, shortly after breakfast, I said, as if it had just occurred to me, "That Catani is a very pretty girl, isn't she?"

The Guahibo, not breaking the regular beat of his paddling, nodded.

"Like you, she's a long way from the Meta, isn't she?"

He nodded again. "Yes," he said, "we are both a very long way, but I am returning now, and she will never return." After that he was silent again.

However, in the lazy days which followed and after a daily bribe of one of my few remaining cigars, the story finally came out.

The Guahibo had been adopted by Catani's mother when he was only six, a year older than Catani. No legal procedure was necessary; the mother simply decided that she wanted a servant, offered his family a little money, and he was hers for life.

Catani's parents, he said, were Russian. He did not know how they had come to the Meta or when. They were typical of the hundreds of Eastern European families who can be found throughout the jungles of Amazonia. Her father, the Guahibo said, often spoke vaguely of diamond mines, but he did not know if that was the reason he had left Russia with his wife for the long, uncomfortable journey across the Atlantic.

As it was, he ran a store much like Joaquín's in a settlement on the Meta. He was, the Indian said, an ugly man, with a huge mustache, a burly body, and an uncontrollable temper. When he had been drinking, which was most of the time, he often beat Catani's mother, from whom the girl must have inherited her beauty. The mother, a small, dark woman, died when Catani was ten.

After that Catani and the Guahibo were inseparable.

Then, when Catani was fourteen, a spark from the cooking fire in the kitchen hut ignited the straw roof of the main hut, and in a few minutes it had burned to the ground. At the same time the store caught on fire, and it also was destroyed. Only a few belongings and a little merchandise were saved.

Since Catani's father was gone at the time—he often was, and during his absences the Guahibo was her only protection—the Indians who worked for him left the same afternoon as the fire. They knew of his temper and were afraid that he would beat and possibly even kill them.

For almost a week Catani and the Guahibo slept on the cold ground in the only hut which had not been destroyed.

When the father returned he had a growth of beard, was red-eyed, and obviously still drunk. He looked at the ruins of what remained of his possessions, stooped, picked up a stick, and began beating Catani. The Guahibo, who was then fifteen years old, tried to intervene, and Catani's father knocked him to the ground and began kicking him. He nearly died of his wounds.

In the days that followed Catani's father drank constantly; he lay in the grass shelter, muttering to himself and nightly falling into a drunken stupor on the ground. The Guahibo slept in one corner of the shelter, Catani and her father on the opposite side.

One night the Indian was awakened by a terrified scream from Catani, and he rushed to her side. There was a man in the hammock beside her, and the Guahibo reached for him. The man raised himself, reached out his foot, and kicked the Indian in the groin. Then he began cursing, and the Guahibo crawled back to his hammock.

The voice had been that of Catani's father.

A few months after I left the Meta, Catani, her father, and the Guahibo started south; they traveled by dugout and by foot; they slept in the open at night, Catani and her father a little away from the Indian. After several weeks of travel they arrived at a small settlement on the Guaviare River, about three hundred miles to the south. Here the father, with the help of the Indians, built himself a new hut and a small store and set himself up in business again. He was not drinking just then, and the store prospered. He also had some success in rubber trading.

Meantime Catani was twice pregnant by her father; like many Indian women, she went into the jungle and killed both children at birth.

Often when Catani's father was away the Guahibo was left in charge of the store and of the daughter. Catani often teased him about the fact that he had never made love to a girl, the Indian said, and during one of her father's absences he lost his innocence. After that they often shared Catani's hammock when they were alone together.

One day about a year and a half after their arrival on the Guaviare, Catani's father came home accompanied by a chubby young trader who immediately fell in love with her. Although he knew she was her father's mistress, he ignored it. He returned to the settlement every few weeks, sometimes with an excuse of business, often without.

Eventually Catani's father became suspicious, and one afternoon he followed them into the jungle where he found them in each other's arms. He began beating the young trader, who managed to escape in the jungle. The father chased him for miles with a shotgun but was unable to catch up with him. Then the father returned to the settlement, and that night he again nearly beat Catani to death.

Nevertheless, with the help of some sympathetic Indians, all of whom hated Catani's father, the young trader managed to arrange a rendezvous with her in the jungle, and he asked her to run away with him.

After a few days of indecision Catani agreed, and one night, while her father was snoring drunkenly in his hammock, she and the Guahibo crept out of the hut. An hour later they were in the dugout of the young trader, headed down river.

They ended their journey four hundred miles to the south, in the area of the Caquetá River. Here, the young trader felt sure, Catani's father would never find them. For a while Catani was completely happy, probably for the first time in her life. The trader had built a small hut. For more than a year she was a good wife to him—though, naturally, they were not married. She kept the hut scrupulously clean; she cooked the meals; she worked with the Indian women; she played hostess to the occasional travelers who passed through the settlement.

Then a man named Joaquín arrived and asked to be put up for the night. He was, he said, on his way to the Putumayo, an area which he indicated was filled with adventure and romance.

As he talked he kept looking at Catani. Every word was for her, and he spoke well. Besides, he was to her a handsome man, representing a world she had never known. He talked about Manáos, where there were broad, tree-lined boulevards, an opera house and several movie theaters, cafés at which one could sit on the sidewalks under an awning and drink red wine, and shops where beautiful dresses were available.

Joaquín left the morning after his arrival, but when the young trader was out of the hut for a moment he told Catani he would return someday.

When Joaquín returned three months later the young trader

was on a rubber-hunting expedition, and Catani and the Guahibo were alone in the hut. That night Catani asked the Guahibo to sleep in her room near her. Joaquín frightened her, she said; he undressed her with his eyes, and he caused her to feel strange emotions which she could neither understand nor control.

The next morning Joaquín sent the Guahibo to his dugout, and the Indian returned with a huge wooden chest filled with merchandise. He placed it on the floor of the hut, and Joaquín opened it and lifted out two dresses, one red, one green. Both were Catani's size, and he asked her to choose between them.

She hesitated for a long time, her eyes wide with admiration. Both dresses were beautiful, she said, and she had never seen such brightly colored cloth, cloth so soft to the touch, cloth that would feel so smooth against the skin.

Finally she decided on the green.

Then Joaquín picked up both dresses and placed them in her arms. They were hers, he said.

Catani burst into tears. She could not possibly accept them, she insisted; this was too much payment for a few nights of lodging.

However, it was not difficult to persuade her, and the Guahibo realized that Catani would not ask for his protection that night. She shared her hammock with Joaquín, who had given the Indian a pair of trousers and a shirt.

Two days later Catani, Joaquín, and the Guahibo started toward the Putumayo by dugout.

On the third day of their voyage down river the young trader caught up with them. He was in a small, fast dugout accompanied by two Indian guides from the settlement on the Caquetá.

As he approached Joaquín pulled his dugout into shore and waited calmly on the bank of the river.

The young trader, a short, pudgy man with a kind face and a

weak chin, drew his dugout up nearby. He got out and walked up to Catani. She lowered her eyes and looked away.

"I am taking this woman with me," said Joaquín, staring belligerently at the young trader. "She wants to go."

The young trader glanced once again at Catani. "Is this true?" he asked.

Catani, still not looking at him, nodded her head slowly.

The young trader nervously fingered the pistol at his belt. No one spoke, but Joaquín showed no fear. He merely continued to stare at the trader.

After a moment the young trader turned, climbed back into his dugout, and without looking back went once more in the direction from which he had come.

As the Guahibo described the scene, I realized that the trader must have loved Catani very much.

A few days later Joaquín and Catani arrived at the settlement on the Putumayo where I had seen her for the second time.

When I asked the young Guahibo why, after so many years, he was leaving Catani, he stared into the water. Then he said almost the same thing as the missionary.

"That woman," he said, "is of the devil."

I knew then that he loved her too.

The Guahibo's story ended there, but I knew I would hear more of Catani. There was no reason for knowing it, but I did.

It was the eighth day since our leaving the settlement in which I had seen Catani, and it was hot. Every day is hot along the Putumayo. It had rained a little in the morning, but then it always does that, too.

Somehow that particular morning the cold rain before dawn followed by the oppressive sun affected all of us. By noon we were exhausted, and when we came to a particularly cool-looking and inviting spot on the river, we stopped. While the Huitotos and the Guahibo prepared lunch, I took one of my cameras, my .22 rifle, and a machete and entered the jungle. I had nothing in particular in mind. I might, I thought, snap a few pictures; I might come across a wild pig; I might be able to shoot a tapir. More likely I would return to the dugout empty-handed.

I did—but not quite in the way I expected.

I proceeded cautiously through the gloom of the jungle. There was no trail, and every five or ten yards I cut a mark on one of the trees with my machete. Otherwise I would never have been able to find my way back through the grayness.

I must have walked for half an hour, stopping occasionally to listen to the angry chatter of a jungle parrot. Then I came to a spot where the ground was soft and wet, leading, I was sure, to a nearby swamp. A little way ahead two trees had fallen, and here the sun penetrated the gloom like a giant spotlight; underneath the ground was clear of vegetation.

As I neared the clearing I heard the sound of what I first thought was a monkey's gibberish. I quickly returned my machete to its sheath and with my rifle at the ready crept noiselessly forward. The position from which the sound came seemed to shift, now a little to the left, then a little to the right. I looked at the branches overhead, at the damp ground underneath, and then on every side of me; at first I saw nothing, but as my eyes completed their second round of inspection I gasped with terror.

In the bushes to my left, no more than a yard away, was the head of an anaconda, its slimy tongue rhythmically slithering in and out of its mouth, its fixed, glassy eyes staring straight at me.

The snake's neck was retracted into an S-shape, like a giant spring about to be released. Then, with a movement so sudden it was almost invisible, the anaconda struck at me with its huge, disjointed mouth.

Instinctively I had raised my rifle and as the snake struck it caught the weapon and part of my shirt sleeve between its teeth. In another instant it attempted to wrap its body around me; instead it hit me on the shoulder and knocked me to the ground. I dropped the rifle and so did the snake, but my sleeve was still tangled in its slanting teeth. I gave one hard jerk and tore the shirt loose. Then I tried to rise, but my left foot was imprisoned under the snake's heavy coils. The moment I realized I was trapped the snake retracted its neck for a second strike.

By this time I had pulled the machete out of its sheath. Fortunately it was a sturdy one, and before the monster could strike again I had aimed a heavy blow at its head.

It writhed and hissed angrily.

I next pulled myself into a sitting position, and with the help of my free hand tried to pull out my imprisoned foot. Instead I managed only to get it more deeply imbedded in the monster's coils. I again hit it on the head, this time desperately. I was trembling; my body was bathed in perspiration, and I realized that my strength was fading fast.

As I saw the head of the snake retract once more above my head, I fell flat on the ground and pushed at the snake's body with my free leg. It hesitated momentarily.

After that I was no longer frightened. My mind worked with perfect precision, and even the trembling disappeared. I sat up, and for a third time hit the anaconda with my machete; this time the blow was effective. The snake shivered, and blood oozed from the wound.

From then on I hit the snake blow after blow; I have no idea how many times. Finally I felt the pressure on my foot released, but then a single coil of the snake wrapped around my ankle.

Its body now stretched straight except for the coil around my ankle and the anaconda began dragging me through the underbrush. As it went its body became thinner and lengthened considerably. It was then about ten inches in diameter at its thickest and nearly forty feet long.

I tried reaching its tail with my machete, but the heavy undergrowth interfered. My face and most of my body became a mass of scratches and bruises as we went along. Then, when I had been dragged perhaps twenty-five yards, my heart seemed to stop beating for a minute or two.

Straight ahead was a small lake. About ten yards before the anaconda came to the water it reached a fallen tree trunk; as it slithered over the trunk I braced my other foot hard against it and succeeded in swinging my machete against the snake's tail. The coil immediately dropped away from the snake, and without stopping the anaconda continued on toward the lake.

In minutes it had disappeared beneath the water.

I kicked the still-wriggling live piece of snake—which must have measured about a foot and a half—from around my ankle and threw it aside. Then I tried to return the machete to its sheath. It was impossible. My hand was so tightly clasped around the machete's handle that I could not force myself to let go of the weapon which had saved my life.

I placed my free hand against a tree trunk to rest my body, and as I did so a conga ant which must have been more than an inch long bit me hard on the hand. Two tiny drops of blood dropped lazily to the ground.

At this point I laughed, partly in relief, partly in hysteria. I laughed for what must have been several minutes, and finally was able to return the machete to its sheath. After that I started back to the dugout, carefully following the marks I had made on the trees.

The next morning I had completely recovered, and we continued our journey.

My encounter with the anaconda was by no means unusual. When a man goes hunting alone or travels along a river in the Amazonia, if he is never heard of again, his disappearance is almost always attributed to this huge snake. The anaconda usually swallows its victims whole, then goes underwater to digest its prey.

Naturally, there are a lot of legends about the anaconda, some true, most of them false. For one thing there is considerable disagreement about its size. Technical zoological books insist that the snake—which often takes a hundred years to attain its full size—never reaches more than thirty-five feet in length. Most experienced travelers disagree.

On a more recent expedition in the Putumayo area I saw a snake coiled on the ground which must have measured fifty-five feet in length. I didn't get close enough to make more than an estimate, however. A few minutes earlier the snake had strangled an Indian, then vomited his body in a lake where it could be seen floating down river.

As my guides and I watched from a distance, the noise the snake made sounded like the report of a high-caliber rifle. This was a variation from the usual hissing sound it emits when it is angered and exhales air.

In the llanos the anacondas often devour six-month-old calves.

Several years ago a storekeeper in Barranquilla, Colombia, kept a pet anaconda about fifteen feet long. Whenever he left his store unattended, the anaconda would curl itself on one side of the cash register; thus, although the door was always left unlocked, there was never a robbery.

One day the storekeeper became ill, and he insists that the worried anaconda slithered across the street and persuaded a neighbor's wife to follow it back to the store by tugging at her apron with its mouth.

After the storekeeper married, his wife understandably resented the snake and treated it badly. On his return from a business trip he found that the anaconda had strangled his wife. He took out a revolver and shot the anaconda.

5

A damp, biting wind swept across the bleak plaza, and the dark-skinned young policeman shivered and drew his thin jacket closer about him. Then he once again placed his hands in his pockets.

As he turned his body frontwards, a dilapidated Chevrolet coupé without a top ground to an agonized stop and waited. A moment later the policeman shifted sideways, and the coupé lurched on.

It was five in the afternoon, but there were only a few other cars on the streets, most of them grouped around the plaza, trucks, cabs, and small buses with drivers who were waiting for passengers on the long trek to Quito. There is never much traffic in Tulcán, but there is a traffic policeman on duty all day at the intersection in the center of town, turning frontwards as a stop signal, sideways when he decides a car can proceed. He seldom removes his hands from his pockets. There is always a high wind in Tulcán, and it is always cold.

Tulcán is just across the Ecuadorean border; it is only six miles from Ipiales, Colombia, separated by the Río Carchi. The river at this point forms into a kind of bottleneck, and beyond are the always forbidding mountains of Ecuador. There is not much love lost between the two towns. The citizens feel about each other somewhat the same as the residents of St. Paul feel about those who live in Minneapolis.

Both Tulcán and Ipiales are small; both are cold, and both are desolate. Neither will ever become much of a tourist attraction.

It was late January; I had worked hard all winter, and I hadn't had time for even a short expedition the summer before. I was tired and a little irritable, and ten days before, after dinner one evening, Madeline had got the huge, sweat-stained map of South America out of my desk and handed it to me.

"What's that?" I asked foolishly.

"That," said Madeline, "is the map on which you're going to work out your next expedition. You need to get away for a while."

"Well," I said, "if you insist." Madeline laughed, and I began to outline the details of an expedition I'd been dreaming about for years, ever since I'd first heard about the Jívaros, the head-shrinking Indians of Ecuador.

A few days later I'd booked passage on a flight from Bogotá to Ipiales, and that afternoon I'd crossed the border into Tulcán. The rest of the trip would be by land.

As usual I'd had a little trouble with customs. The officials wanted me to deposit an inordinate sum of money to bring my three Rolleiflexes and two Bolex movie cameras into Ecuador. Instead of arguing I used a trick that never yet has failed.

I opened one of my cases and removed a series of pictures I'd taken a few years before in Africa. They were mainly of native girls, and most of them wore very scanty costumes or no costumes at all. The pictures were hugely successful.

The customs officials giggled like schoolgirls and appreciatively nudged each other in the ribs.

The chief of customs guffawed. "I'll be glad to carry your tripod," he said, "if you guarantee you can take pictures like that. Where are you going?"

I told him to the Jívaro country.

"Well," he said, laughing, "your shrunken head will probably be on sale in Quito in a few weeks, but, if you want to go, I won't stop you."

Then he made a list of the equipment I was taking, and a few minutes later I was on my way across the plaza to the Granada Hotel.

The young policeman nodded pleasantly, and I glanced down the now-darkened main street of Tulcán. There were only a few dimly lighted stores, a single liquor shop with a neon sign, a movie theater, and, around one corner, a house of prostitution. The street looked drab and depressed, and even the people shuffling home from work seemed colorless and without spirit. No one looked up; there was not even any conversation. It was too cold for that. As the darkness grew, the cold wind intensified.

When I entered the dank lobby of the Granada, a small man with the face of a mischievous monkey anxiously watched the two boys bring in my luggage. Then he stepped forward and grinned eerily. He had only two widely separated teeth, both black and decayed-looking, one in his upper jaw, the other in his lower.

"The mister is maybe going to Quito, yes?" he asked.

I nodded coldly.

"Then," said the small man, scratching himself vigorously under his left armpit, "maybe the mister wants to go with me?"

I shook my head.

"I'll make arrangements tomorrow," I said.

He shrugged and philosophically stepped aside as I walked up to the desk to register.

I have stayed in filthy, bug-infested hotels on four continents now, but the Granada is among the worst. It is a loosely constructed, unpainted building with inside balconies built around a dingy dining room. There must be thirty rooms, but there is a single shower and toilet which when I was there could not have been cleaned in months. Naturally there was no hot water, and the cold flowed from the tap only briefly, then trickled to a halt.

There was no window in my room, and the single bed had no spring mattress, only a few carelessly placed wooden slats. In addition there were two straight-backed chairs, and a night table with a jug on top. The only light came from a single naked bulb in the center of the room.

I had decided to spend all of the next day in Tulcán, but I took one look at the room, turned around, and went outside again. I decided to leave as early as possible in the morning. Among its other disadvantages, Tulcán has a nine-thousand-foot-elevation above sea level. I was dressed for the tropics.

As soon as I stepped outside, the little man I had met in the lobby rushed up to me, his two teeth gleaming in the moonlight.

"Maybe the mister wants to talk business now, no?" he asked.

"Maybe," I said. From then on he was Mr. Maybe. I never did find out his real name.

"What's your deal?" I asked.

He hesitated, as a shrewd trader should. "For you," he said, "and only you because I would find your company most pleasurable, for you I charge twenty-five sucres for the trip to Quito. For your luggage"—he paused again, and I knew that in his mind he was weighing each piece and doubling his usual charge—"for your luggage, fifty sucres, maybe no?"

"Maybe no," I said, starting to walk away. "I will pay fifty sucres for me and my luggage, and that's all."

I began to round the corner; instantly Mr. Maybe was beside me. "Forty-five sucres for the luggage, maybe no?" he began. I shook my head.

We settled on a total price of fifty sucres.

"You give me money now, maybe?" asked the little man.

"I'll give you the money tomorrow," I said.

His shoulders drooped sadly. "I have maybe to buy some things for the babies," he said.

"How many babies?" I asked.

"I have three," he said, smiling again.

I gave Maybe fifteen sucres, and he promised to pick me up at the Granada at four the next morning.

I don't remember sleeping that night; I do remember tossing, turning, scratching, and shivering, but I must have dozed off for a few minutes because I was unconscious when the boy knocked on my door at three-thirty. By five minutes to four I was standing outside the hotel, my luggage piled high beside me.

Exactly at four I heard a rattle down the street. I looked up and saw what must have been one of the first trucks Henry Ford ever manufactured approaching wearily and noisily. It had only one dim light, which flickered nervously. Fifty yards away the brakes were squeakily applied.

When he stepped down Mr. Maybe seemed as surprised as I was that the truck had stopped more or less in front of the hotel.

"You don't mean I'm supposed to ride in that?" I asked. Maybe nodded emphatically.

"It is a very good truck," he said. "I have made many trips in

it, and I have always got to where I was going." He patted the
fender affectionately.

I shrugged. "Okay," I said, and as Maybe and the boy from
the hotel began loading my luggage I walked around to the
other side of the truck. There was no fender, and when I turned
the handle of the door it refused to budge. I applied more force,
and this time the handle turned. Also the door dropped off the
frame and clattered to the sidewalk.

Mr. Maybe ran around the truck shouting, "Not that door,
the other one." But it was too late. He picked up a screw driver
and put the door back on, then led me around to the other side.
In the darkness in the back of the truck I made out several forms,
and a baby who had apparently been awakened by the clanging
of the door cried softly.

I climbed in the front, and Mr. Maybe seated himself behind
the wheel and turned on the ignition. Then the motor roared;
the cabin started to vibrate; a squeak of the clutch announced the
take-off; I braced myself, and we started down the bleak road,
lighted only by the single weak headlight.

By daylight I realized what I was in for. The narrow road from
Tulcán to Quito is built on the edge of a continuous deep precipice, stretching several thousand feet straight down. On the curve
Mr. Maybe's face contorted dangerously, and he perspired profusely as he turned the steering wheel, which was too tight to be
maneuvered easily.

Each time we passed another vehicle my heart stopped beating
because there seemed to be no more than an inch or two between
the outer wheels of the truck and the edge of the precipice. To
make matters worse, we always passed at full speed because of
the faulty brakes.

At seven Maybe stopped the truck by the side of the road and announced that breakfast would be served. Then, as they emerged from the back, he introduced me to his wife, a fat, phlegmatic woman with heavy features, a boy who was probably no more than six months old, and the other two "babies," one a girl of perhaps thirteen, the other probably two years older. Both had fully developed figures and a kind of ephemeral beauty.

They chatted gaily as they cooked and, since I had gone to school in the United States, wanted to know if I was acquainted with Miss Joan Crawford, the only movie actress with whom they were familiar.

When we started on again, the radiator of the truck began to steam, and every time we reached a rise in the road the motor groaned even more loudly than usual and threatened to stop altogether. Occasionally Mr. Maybe broke into song or whistled; the baby whimpered constantly; the road sometimes narrowed into what was little more than a cowpath, and the precipices seemed to deepen. Nevertheless, we continued on.

By dusk, when we pulled into the outskirts of Quito, I was exhausted. When I stepped out in front of the Majestic Hotel, I shook Mr. Maybe's calloused hand and gave him a tip of ten sucres for having got me safely to my destination. Then I said good-by to the girls, went up to my room, lay down for a nap, and did not wake up until after eight the next morning.

The capital of Ecuador is a boom town. It is growing almost as fast as Los Angeles, California. It is even higher in the Andes than Tulcán, and there are a hundred churches and a dozen monasteries and convents, one of which, the San Francisco convent, is one of the largest in the world.

The streets of the city wander up and down, drunkenly and without reason; there are thousands of statues and almost all of the houses, even the poorest, have patios. Some are used only as chicken pens, others as gardens, with fountains, trees, and broad expanses of grass that is unendingly green.

The residents call it "The City of Eternal Spring," which is not really true, but it comes close. There are mountains on every side, many of them topped with snow; the squares in which the city is laid out are sprinkled with the brightest flowers, which seem to bloom all year round, and day and night the sound of the bells of a dozen churches can be heard echoing against the sides of the mountains.

Quito is the oldest city in the Western Hemisphere and probably the most beautiful.

My only real business there was to obtain a gun permit, which should have been easy. However, the automobile races were going on at the time, and, since this was the most important event of the year, nobody could be expected to take much interest in anything else. When I went to the police, the young sergeant in charge of issuing gun permits was charming and affable, but, although all he had to do was take a look at my revolver and write his name on a piece of paper, he said he would be unable to get around to it for at least four days. By that time the race, which begins in Quito and ends in Caracas, would be over, and the sergeant would know whether he was a rich man or still poor. The race over the narrow mountain roads of the Andes lasts a week, and sometimes one or two drivers are killed. The event is as important to Ecuador as the bullfights are to Spain. Everybody makes at least one bet on the outcome.

Since I had a four-day wait, I decided to use the time to visit the Colorados Indians, whose nearest settlement was only six hours from Quito. The trip was by truck; it was in slightly better condition than Maybe's, but the road was just as precarious as that from Tulcán. On the slopes of the mountainside bordering the road were tiny farms, most of them less than an acre in size and with miniature one-room huts clinging precariously to the nearly perpendicular earth. I saw a few cows, a number of which every year lose their footing and roll down the mountains into the valley below, some banana trees, and tiny, gardenlike squares of almost arid land.

I arrived in Santo Domingo de los Colorados on Sunday, which was market day. The streets were crowded with people, many of them already drunk. A man whose voice had a pleasant whiskey huskiness was describing the plots of the movies at the town's two theaters; he told the stories in such detail that there was no real reason to see the movies. Two paint-smeared Colorados were embracing drunkenly in front of one of the bars; from inside a juke box was blaring the distortion of a Spanish folk song; in the shadows of the building lingered two no longer young prostitutes, smiling sadly and hopelessly.

Santo Domingo de los Colorados was having a quiet Sunday afternoon. Ten years before things would have been quite different. At that time the village was a refuge for scores of criminals, thieves, rapists, and murderers. On weekdays they hid in the surrounding hills, but on Sundays they invaded the bars for a day of drinking. One or two murders occurred weekly. The local citizenry usually locked themselves in their houses, but if one made the mistake of venturing out, he was ordered to have a drink. To have refused would have been a possibly fatal breach of good manners. Once when one of the two local policemen tried to sneak across the street without attracting the attention of the bandits, he was seen and offered a free drink; when he refused, five shots were fired at his feet. The policeman immediately changed his mind.

One youthful thief was particularly troublesome; he stole hundreds of sucres' worth of property from the Colorados, who were helpless in dealing with him. At one point one of the local chieftains took up a collection and gave it to the thief in return for his promise to leave the settlement alone. The thief took the money, but returned a few weeks later for another raid.

Then the Colorados found out that he wanted to go to La Esmeralda, and the chief promised to show him a path on which, the chief said, he would not meet up with the police. The chief did not mention that the path led to a desolate spot called "La Posa del Tigre" (The Lodge of the Jaguar).

There were hundreds of jaguars in the area, and the Indians never expected to hear of the thief again. The Colorados are a peaceful people and do not believe in killing anyone, even their worst enemies; however, they reasoned that if the thief were devoured by a jaguar they could not be considered responsible.

However, a month later the thief was back, healthier and more troublesome than ever. So the Indians gave a party, ostensibly to celebrate his return. Since it is a custom to leave all weapons outside the hut on such a spree, the thief laid both his six-shooters on the ground and proceeded to get noisily drunk. Then the police, who had been notified of the festivities by the Colorados, moved in and just before the thief passed out arrested him.

In the months that followed the Ecuadorean authorities killed or captured most of the lawbreakers. Since then Santo Domingo de los Colorados has been reasonably safe to live in.

There is not much privacy in the Astoria Hotel in Santo Domingo; a huge, barnlike barracks has been divided into stalls by wallboard partitions not quite reaching either the floor or the ceiling; half a mile behind the hotel are a primitive outdoor toilet and a rustic shower.

After registering I spent the afternoon on the balcony, watching the growing drunkenness in the square below.

At dusk, as I was about to fall asleep, I felt a gentle tap on my shoulder and looked up. Standing above me was a thin, muscular man with soft eyes and a gentle smile. He introduced himself as Jacome, guide and world traveler. I later learned that he had been as far as Quito, ten years before.

"I hear," he said, "that you want to visit the Colorados."

I nodded.

"Then," he said, "I will guide you."

The trip was only four hours by horseback, but Jacome indicated that without him I'd probably get lost and die of starvation; so I agreed.

We left early the next morning. As we started off the streets of Santo Domingo were still crowded with drunken Colorados, some of whom were sleeping it off on the sidewalks and, occasionally, in the middle of the street.

The Colorados are a reasonably civilized people; they are also calculating businessmen and often incurable drunkards.

They are called Colorados ("The Red Ones" in Spanish) because the men paint their hair red with a dye made from *achote* seeds. When the paint dries the hair becomes stiff and makes a kind of visor in front of their eyes so that when they walk they have to hold their heads back in order to see where they're going. Both men and women paint thin horizontal lines of black on their faces and slightly thicker lines on their bodies. Both sexes also blacken their teeth by chewing a plant called *ueva* which also prevents decay. In addition they wear short, hand-woven cloths with horizontal stripes around their middles and, if they can afford them, bright kerchiefs around their necks. Their faces are usually lean, their noses hooked, their lips thin; they often have an almost Mongolian look about them. In addition most of the men wear a thin stick about six inches long through a hole drilled in their noses when they reach the age of puberty.

In the jungle, of course, they dress that way because they know no other, but around Santo Domingo and other large villages they recognize that they are colorful and charge the tourists for taking their pictures. If business is good, and it usually is, every Sunday they buy all the aguardiente they can drink. On Monday morning their hair is disheveled, the red paint smeared over their bodies, the horizontal stripes blurred, the colorful cloths a tangled mass of rags.

We edged our horses around the prostrate bodies in the street, and in a few minutes Jacome and I were in the cool mist of the jungle. He was an excellent guide; he spoke only when spoken to or to point out a rare bird or an unusual bush or tree. He appreciated silence and understood it.

"Compadre" Julio was a tall man, a little under six feet, with a thin, lithe body, an almost unlined face, and the burning eyes of a fanatic. He must have been in his late thirties; he lived in a large house, divided into two parts, one of which was used for weaving and cooking and was open to the weather, the other enclosed by bark walls. Julio and his two wives slept in the latter. The only other house in the settlement was supported by bamboo poles, and it was here that Julio's patients stayed while waiting to be cured. Surrounding the clearing were cultivated plots of land on which were grown yuca and bananas, the principal food of the Colorados, and beyond, on every side, was the thick, dark jungle.

Julio was not too cordial at first, but I told him that I had come all the way from Bogotá to consult him. For years, I said, I had suffered from a painful crick in my back; I had consulted the most famous doctors in the world, in Quito, in Bogotá, and even in Boston and New York which, as he perhaps did not know, were in a country far to the north called the United States. None of them had been able to help me; then I had heard of Julio, and I had been told that he could cure any illness. That was why I was here.

Julio nodded curtly. He did not seem surprised or pleased by what I had said.

Of course he could cure me, he said; he asked no questions about the location or origins of my imagined pain. He just told me to appear with his many other patients in a shelter inside a second, smaller clearing a few hundred yards away from the larger one.

I should, Julio went on, arrive a little before midnight because the spirits would not respond until that hour. He knew because he had tried summoning them earlier, always without success, and, if anyone could do it, it would be he because he had worked for years to reach his present position. For instance, he said, he had never been able to eat any food containing salt. Worse yet, as a young man, he had been put through months of tests to see if he qualified as a witch doctor and during all that time he had been unable to make love to a girl. Moreover, if a girl came to sleep in his hut—and he indicated that there had been many—he had to leave the hut and sleep elsewhere. Naturally, he went on, when he had qualified as a witch doctor, he had immediately taken two wives, and, if he were able to afford it, he would have at least one more. Then he dismissed me.

A little before midnight I appeared at Julio's *hospital*: It consisted of four poles and a straw roof; the only illumination was a short, flickering candle on a long, low table hewn out of the trunk of a palm tree before which Julio sat on a log. There were nine other people in the shelter, most of them old, all of them volubly suffering from something or other, mostly from invisible maladies. An elderly man in his late fifties supported himself on a single crutch, and an emaciated middle-aged woman hobbled along on a cane; one of her legs was twisted beneath her. The patients were all obviously poor and uneducated, but their eyes shone with a naïve faith which made me uncomfortable. They must have been very much like the people who once crowded into Aimee Semple McPherson's temple in Los Angeles.

They sat on blankets on the ground, and I hung my hammock between two of the poles and sat down to watch. The ceremonies would last until dawn, and while each "cure" was taking place the others could sleep if they wished, although nobody did.

Exactly at midnight Julio reached under the table and took out a small, rough bag made from the skin of a tapir. He removed a dozen tiny talismans roughly carved out of stone, each representing a different animal or an ax. He laid the figures in neat rows on the table in front of him; then he brought several good-sized bottles of various colored liquids from under the table and placed them on top, just behind the stone figures. After that he closed his eyes and began to moan rhythmically, jerking his body backwards and forwards, occasionally interrupting himself with high screams and the sudden flow of a language that seemed to consist of no more than a dozen undecipherable words. At the same time he lovingly passed his hands over the talismans. Finally he stopped suddenly, and there was silence in the shelter. No one appeared even to breathe.

Then from each of the bottles he took a huge swallow of liquid, spraying each over all of the stone figures. Next he filled a calabash with a murky white fluid and passed it around, telling each of us to take a swallow. The liquid was a narcotic made from a jungle vine called *nepe* by the Colorados, though other tribes in the Amazonia have more colorful names for it. If drunk in quantity, its effect is about the same as that of marijuana.

I swallowed only a little but for at least half an hour thereafter felt lightheaded and giddy.

A few minutes later Julio motioned for me to come forward and seat myself on a tree trunk a few feet from him. With a tiny twig he began to beat me lightly, first on the top of my head, gradually working down my back. This, he explained, was to purify my soul and to drive out the evil spirits which lurked in my back. The beating lasted for at least fifteen minutes and was rather pleasant. The twig felt something like a Chinese back scratcher.

After that Julio took a swallow of a suspicious-looking yellow fluid from one of the bottles and, before I knew what was happening, sprayed my face with it. Next he began beating me again, this time mainly on top of the head, meantime muttering further high-pitched incantations which he asked me to repeat after him. By this time I could scarcely keep my eyes open, and when Julio reached for a second bottle, this one filled with a liquid which had the color and consistency of human blood, I rose, stretched myself, and announced that a miracle had been wrought. After all these years I was completely cured; it would be unnecessary for him to spray me with a mouthful of the red liquid.

Julio was not in the least surprised. In all his years as a witch doctor, he said, he had never yet failed to effect a cure.

Later that night one of the elderly men was sprayed, first with the unpleasantly yellow fluid, second with vegetable juice mixed with the scrapings of what allegedly were jaguars' fangs; however, when Julio reached for the reddish liquid the man hurriedly said that it was unnecessary; he no longer felt weak, he said; he was, in fact, filled with energy, and he jumped up and down several times to prove it.

However, I noticed that minutes after he reached his blanket he was snoring loudly.

Another man, who must have been in his early forties and complained of impotence, was rubbed with a liquid made from vegetable juice and a powder said to have been scraped from the bone penis of two small, monkeylike animals, the *cuchucho* and the *cusumbi*. This, too, Julio sprayed into the man's face, after which the patient insisted that he was no longer impotent.

At dawn Julio stopped abruptly and declared that the healing spirits had fled; he would be able to perform no more miracles until midnight, and he advised everyone except a gnarled old man to get a good day's sleep and return.

I stayed behind with Julio and the old man and shortly after sunrise we went outside the shelter to a large round hole, inside of which was a roughly made wooden oven in which half a dozen good-sized stones were heating over a hot fire. As he removed each stone, Julio carried it between two sticks and placed the old man's rheumatic legs over it; when the stone cooled he brought another and returned the first to the fire for reheating. After about an hour the old man happily stretched his legs and said that the pains were gone. I was inclined to think he was telling the truth. Julio's treatment for rheumatism, performed without talismans, sprays, or incantations, is not, after all, so very different from that given in most modern hospitals.

That afternoon, after a few hours of sleep, I watched a Colorado burial. The body, that of a young girl who had died from a mysterious and undiagnosed disease, was placed in a shallow grave in the midst of the jungle and covered over. Then a large stick was placed horizontally over the grave, and a meal of yuca and bananas was hung on the stick to feed the girl's soul, a process that would be repeated until the stick broke. After that it is presumed that the spirit has fled. The ants and other insects are well fed during the interim.

When I got back to Quito the young police sergeant was downcast; he had lost a great deal of money on the races. However, he said, my gun permits were ready. All I had to do was to buy a large number of stamps at the post office and bring them to him. When I gave him the stamps, he put half of them on the permits; the others he openly pocketed, no doubt to help make up for some of his losses.

The next morning I left by bus for El Puyo, certainly the least civilized and ugliest village in all of Ecuador and located at the entrance to the Jívaro country.

There are three hundred people in El Puyo, all of them poverty-sticken, all discouraged, all without hope. The muddy main street is about a hundred and fifty yards long; there is a stone church with broken steps leading inside, the usual few stores, and a dirty two-story wooden building called the Hotel Camacho. I arrived shortly after dusk, carried my luggage up to the shabby stall which was my room, and then, without unpacking, went to look for a man named Freire, who had been recommended by Jacome as a possible guide for my journey into the Jívaro country.

I found Freire sitting on the steps of his small, unpainted house looking disconsolately into the jungle which threatened to envelop El Puyo on every side. He was a sturdily built little man with a thin, tired face and deep circles under his brown eyes. His right ankle was wrapped in loose, dirty bandages.

When I explained that I wanted to hire him as a guide, he shook his head sadly. It was ridiculous, he said; it was heartbreaking, but after years of traveling through uncharted jungles and up and down almost unnavigable rivers he had, on his way to mass the previous Sunday, turned his ankle on one of the broken steps leading into the church. Thus, he shrugged, he would be unable to accompany me, and he deeply regretted it.

"This," he said, "is the best time of year to visit the Jívaros. The tree they call *huy* is just now flowering, meaning that another year has passed. The wars of revenge will now begin again."

He paused. "You are lucky to be able to see such wars," he went on.

I nodded and smiled wanly. "Is there any possibility that I might have my head shrunk as a result?" I asked.

Señor Freire shrugged. "It is not impossible," he said diplomatically.

"However," he went on, "it is unlikely." Then he explained that the Jívaros kill only for revenge. "Usually," he added. "Such things are not *always* to be depended on. I have known exceptions; I have examined the shrunken heads of friends."

"What do you mean, wars of revenge?" I asked.

The Jívaros, Señor Freire continued, live in small settlements scattered throughout the jungles; there are seldom more than thirty persons in each, sometimes as few as ten. A typical war might begin when, say, a group of Jívaros from Settlement A killed a resident of Village B. The next year the residents of B would automatically kill as many citizens of A as possible, and the year thereafter A would retaliate, and so on. In most cases, he said, the origins of such wars are unknown, or forgotten.

When I left Señor Freire that night, he had promised that the next morning he would introduce me to a perfect guide, what he called "a tame Jívaro," and, he went on, one of the most remark-able men in Ecuador.

When I met Severo Vargas in the lobby of the Camacho Hotel the next morning, I immediately agreed. Severo would command attention anywhere. He is in his mid-sixties and has the body of a heavyweight in perfect condition; he has the broadest shoulders I have ever seen on a man, a deep chest, and an unbelievably small waist. His long, powerful arms hang awkwardly at his sides as if he found them too heavy to lift. He is of medium height and walks with short, lumbering steps. His black eyes have a quiet, penetrating intensity about them; his chin juts out aggressively, and his mouth is usually set in a hard but not unpleasant firm line.

Severo Vargas is the kind of man who conquers continents and builds civilizations. If he were not an almost illiterate Jívaro born in the jungles of Ecuador, he might have become a president or a prime minister or an industrial tycoon.

I liked him instantly, and, fortunately, he seemed to like me, too, although it took him considerably longer to make up his mind.

Since I was having breakfast, I invited Severo and Señor Freire to join me and ordered coffee for them. Then I took out my map and outlined the expedition I had in mind.

Severo listened carefully, not commenting until I had finished. When he spoke, his voice boomed out like that of an opera bari-tone.

"I know all that territory," he said, speaking an untutored Spanish. "They are my people, and"—here he paused a moment for emphasis—"they obey me.

"All of them obey me," he repeated, pointing to the map of the territory with his index finger.

"Will you go with me then?" I asked.

He had been observing me carefully while I talked, and now, before replying, he looked me over again. Several minutes passed before he replied. Finally he nodded.

"I will go with you," he said.

Before he left that morning, Severo and I had agreed on his salary, and he followed me upstairs to examine my luggage. He carefully lifted each piece, mentally calculating its weight. Then he said, "You will need seven porters." I agreed.

"You have no need for worry," he boomed. "I will handle all."

After that, without another word, he lumbered down the stairs, each of which creaked under his weight, and was gone.

I spent the rest of the morning finding out all I could about Severo Vargas; I didn't need any references, but I did want to discover what the people of El Puyo thought of him.

Naturally everyone had an opinion. He was feared, and he was hated, and he was loved, but, without exception, he was respected.

Several people warned me against him; the man was a killer, they said, and, to prove their point, they repeated, the details varying in each instance, the story of an expedition on which Severo had been a guide for two Frenchmen. One Frenchman died on the trip, and many people in El Puyo assumed that Severo had murdered him.

I later found out from Severo himself what had happened.

He had been hired by the two Frenchmen to guide them down the Pastaza to the town of Iquitos in Peru. A few days out a wandering Indian exchanged a leg of deer for some merchandise, and one of the Frenchmen, despite Severo's warning, ate the meat raw. Two days later he died and was buried in the jungle. After that Severo and the surviving Frenchman went on to Iquitos, where Severo had been promised he would be paid. However, the Frenchman confessed that he didn't have the money; instead, he gave Severo all of the equipment from the expedition as well as a certificate verifying the transfer and stating the reason for his companion's death.

As in all small towns everywhere there is always a good deal of gossip in El Puyo, and when Severo got back with the equipment it was said that he and the surviving Frenchman had robbed the other and killed him.

Since the story could not be proved, Severo's enemies found another way to get even with him for imagined wrongs. The certificate from the surviving Frenchman stated that an electric generator which had been left with a priest at Baños should be turned over to Severo.

The priest was not an honest man. When, after weeks of argument, he turned the crate supposedly containing the motor over to Severo, it was empty. Severo protested, but the priest only laughed. The crate had been empty ever since it was left with him, he said. Severo, who was, the priest went on, only a stupid Indian, had been taken in. Besides, he concluded, what could a Jívaro do with a generator, anyway?

In his anger Severo, who had been baptized at the age of fifty, called the priest a good many highly irreligious names.

A few nights after that, while he slept in his hut in El Puyo, someone who was never identified fired a bullet at Severo through an open window. Miraculously he was not killed; the bullet entered through his right cheek and came out through the back of his head, but he recovered.

One Sunday a few weeks later, after drinking a good deal of aguardiente, Severo openly accused the priest of trying to have him killed. The next morning he was arrested and placed in jail, without charges. He was there two months and twenty days when, after pressure from Ecuadorean authorities in Quito who knew of his work among the Jívaros, he was finally released.

However, Severo was not bitter. When he told me the story, he shrugged philosophically.

"God knows what he does," he said, "for now those who caused me harm are dead, and I am still living."

The priest died of a mysterious and painful disease six months later, and the second Frenchman had been killed in a brawl in Iquitos.

Toward evening of the day I met him, Severo returned to the Hotel Camacho. He had, he said, already hired the porters.

Two would go ahead in a dugout and wait for us at Canelos, the village from which we would start down the Bobonaza River. He, the seven porters, and myself would, Severo explained, go by jungle path to Canelos, carrying the equipment. The river was too turbulent most of the way to risk upsetting the dugout and losing our supplies. I agreed to the plan, and then Severo introduced me to a handsome, muscular boy of seventeen who, he said, wanted to accompany us on the entire expedition. This was his son, Teolo, who looked as stolid and dependable as his father.

We began our expedition the next morning at six. First, as is the custom in the South American jungles, I paid the porters. Otherwise they would not have come. I imagine the practice of payment in advance began in the days when white rubber traders exploited the Indians mercilessly.

Each porter carried bundles weighing about sixty pounds, but, in spite of their slight physiques, neither the weight nor the bulkiness of their burden seemed to bother them. Their bodies were thin, but I knew that they would be able to struggle up and down precarious jungle paths for as long as six or eight hours, pausing only momentarily for rest, and, since Severo had hired them and they respected him, never complaining.

We walked through the silent streets of El Puyo, past the tiny huts in which squalor was dimmed in the darkness, past the church with its broken steps, past the cluster of business houses, their windows covered to protect the merchandise from the early morning sun. In a few minutes we were deep in the jungle, and, as appears to happen at the beginning of every expedition, it began pouring rain. After perhaps an hour, by which time all of us were thoroughly soaked and shivering, the rain stopped. Then, from behind a cloud, the blazing sun emerged, and in the distance was the arch of a rainbow which lasted for only a few minutes.

In the sometimes almost unendurable days of the ten weeks that passed before Teolo, Severo, and I returned to El Puyo I thought a lot about that rainbow.

6

That first day was the worst. It was like those which followed, but it was the worst because it was the beginning. We sometimes climbed steep hills and down again; we sometimes stumbled and fell in the thick undergrowth; we sometimes sank to our knees and deeper in the mud of the barely perceptible paths which would appear out of nowhere; we sometimes hacked new paths with our machetes to avoid flooded areas; we sometimes waded across streams that were shoulder deep, and we were often wet with rain and with perspiration, and always we baked in the sun and shivered in the rain and went on.

By late afternoon we could not have gone much farther, and we were thinking of spending the night in the jungle when, as rarely happens, a clearing was seen, and we soon walked up to a small, neat house which was an ingenious combination of straw, leaves, and wood and was supported by poles. Inside we found a thin, tired woman who could not have been more than thirty-five but looked considerably older, and her teen-aged daughter, a squat, ugly girl who had already been defeated by the jungle. The husband was on a hunting trip, but the wife and daughter were delighted to see us. We were their first visitors in more than a month, they said, and they seldom saw more than a dozen out-siders of any kind in a year. Neither had ever listened to a radio; the daughter had never seen a newspaper, and she had been as far as El Puyo only once in her life.

Strangely enough, however, after I had finished bathing in the Puyo River, which faced the house, an Indian family of four ap-peared, also to be put up for the night. There was a young man, his wife, a seven-year-old daughter, and a six-month-old son, car-ried papoose-fashion by the mother. They had been walking through the jungle for fifteen days, and they had six days to go before reaching the settlement of some friends. They would spend a few days, then make the twenty-one-day trek back to their own settlement, the wife carrying the son on her back, the hus-band the daughter in his arms.

That night before falling asleep I thought of them, and at first it seemed to me they must be crazy to be making such a trip through the jungle. Then I remembered that, after all, I was really doing the same thing, and at the end of my journey I would meet up with the Jívaros, who could hardly be counted on to be friendly. It was I who was insane.

The next day the path was over an uninterrupted series of hills, easy enough to climb but difficult on the descent because we had to brace ourselves to avoid rolling down and at the same time be careful when we grabbed a tree trunk for safety since at least half of them bristled with lengthy, painful thorns.

As usual there was almost no conversation, only the occasional curse of a porter as his hand was jabbed by a thorn, and the constant screams from a basket filled with twenty-five chickens we had bought in El Puyo to roast along the way.

Shortly before dusk we reached a spot just across the Bobonaza River from Canelos, and Severo shouted across to some friends on the other side to bring a dugout to ferry us across.

When we reached the opposite bank of the Bobonaza, I stepped out of the dugout and looked up a low, green promontory on which sat a comfortable, rambling house made of grass and leaves. One side was open to the river, which, just below, made nearly a 180-degree turn, so that the river flowed in back of the house, too. A little further the river casually cascaded over a group of smooth white rocks and dropped into a large water hole, blue-black in the approaching dusk. Half a dozen naked Indian girls were playing in the pool, splashing water on each other and screaming with delight.

Canelos, which was founded early in the eighteenth century by a Spanish missionary, has a mission, a store, and a population of about two hundred people, a handful of whites, a good many more Indians called Alamas who are related to the Jívaros but are by contrast astonishingly mild-mannered.

The next morning our porters returned to El Puyo, and Severo hired another group for the hazardous journey from Canelos to Sarayacu. I spent that next day and the next swimming, lying in

the sun, occasionally reading, once in a while bringing my diary
up to date, but mostly relaxing. I was in no hurry to get to any
place or to return to anything. Instead I wanted to listen to the
muffled murmur of the tiny falls below the grassy hill on which I
lay, to the innocent cries of the Indian girls swimming in the
pool, and to the satisfied screams of the birds in the jungle. I
wanted to breathe in the rich, sweet smell of the flowering trees
and the acrid smoke of the cooking fires. I did not want to think
of the new and more terrible war which, when I left Bogotá, the
newspapers said was inevitable and imminent.

From Canelos to Sarayacu the Bobonaza is never more than a
hundred and twenty feet wide, and, except for an occasional
rapid, extremely easy to navigate. We spent the first night in an
abandoned shelter which was no more than four poles and a roof.
It was a quiet spot when we arrived—but not for long. In unloading the supplies the paddlers came across a can I'd bought at one
of those shabby little joke stores on Broadway near Times Square;
I'd brought it along thinking I might have some fun with it.

As I watched, one of them motioned the others forward; then
he cautiously opened the lid. A second later he and the rest were
screaming and running toward the jungle. It took half the evening to lure them back.

The box contained a cloth snake about twelve feet long which
sprang to its full length as soon as the box was opened.

None of us got much sleep that night as the men opened and
closed the can, slapping their thighs and punching each other in
the ribs with never-ending delight.

The next morning we passed Chambira and Pacayacu, two tiny,
deserted-looking outposts on the left bank of the river. Close up
to each village there would have been the smell of unwashed

bodies and of the obvious lack of a sewer system and of garbage-strewn streets, but, from across the river, there was a cool stillness about both, a green freshness about them.

A little further on I saw a *pava* sitting on the branch of a tree hanging low over the opposite bank. I casually took out my .22 rifle and fired from a distance of a hundred feet.

The bird instantly dropped into the water.

The eyes of the paddlers shone with envy and amazement; even Severo and Teolo seemed impressed, and I was pretty impressed myself—so much so that when one of the paddlers spotted another bird, this one no more than fifty feet away, I unconcernedly aimed and fired at it. The bird flew away.

I shrugged. "That must have been a blank cartridge," I explained to Teolo. He nodded solemnly.

By noon I had fired at at least forty more birds. Each had glanced at me with obvious contempt, then flown away. By one in the afternoon my reputation as a marksman had disappeared, and each paddler in turn had looked first at me, next at my rifle, then away, shaking his head pityingly.

At around three we paused at the small, well-kept hut of a huge Colombian Negro who had the build of a heavyweight and, as is so often the case, the voice and manner of an excitable small boy.

When he heard us coming he ran to the edge of the river and began shouting and waving at us. By the time we had reached the spot where he was standing I already knew that he was thirty-six years old, that he had been living in the hovel behind him for five years, that he had not seen a white man since the previous November (it was now mid-February), that he grew the largest and juiciest oranges in all of the Amazonia, that he had worked in the state of California and in Panama, that as soon as he saved enough money, which would be any month now, he would be off

136

for what he called the "oonite statts" again, and that he was married to—or at any rate living with—the most beautiful woman in all the world, a Huitoto.

The Negro's wife was not beautiful; she was fat; her features were coarse, and, so far as I could see, she had no teeth at all. However, she was gentle, and she obviously loved her husband, and she had borne him nine children of assorted ages, shapes, and colors, including a cocoa-hued daughter of about thirteen who was a real beauty.

In the half hour I spent with the Negro I managed to interrupt him long enough to buy a few oranges—they were, in fact, the largest and juiciest I've ever eaten—and several dozen turtle eggs. However, when I said I couldn't stay overnight at his hut, I thought we might be forcibly detained.

As our dugout proceeded down the river, he was still talking, shouting a little louder as each additional splash of water took us further away.

"I have," he shouted, "been done a great injustice by the police of Ecuador."

After hesitating a moment I shouted back, "Why?"

"They shot me in the leg," he asserted, his voice somewhat fainter now.

"Why?" I repeated, straining my voice a little.

"I was smuggling contraband," he screamed, "and the dogs shot me. They have no sense of justice."

The huge black body was little more than a dot, a dot that listed a little as it went toward the hut because of the unjust police of Ecuador.

After leaving the Negro's hut we did not make very good time; the paddlers would work for two minutes, then rest for five, commenting on the wild life along the banks of the river, pointing out where a jaguar had been shot the year before, or an alligator seen six months previous. Several times I asked Severo to hurry them along, but he only smiled and shook his head.

"When an Indian is not in the mood for paddling," he said, "there will be no paddling."

Finally I lay back in the dugout and went to sleep. Curiosity is an almost essential quality for an explorer; so is a certain amount of what passes for courage, but, more important than either, is patience.

I awakened late in the afternoon when we met up with a large dugout crowded with a dozen or more young Indian males, most of them no more than boys. The entire area to the southwest of us had blazed into a war, they said, and they had only barely escaped being killed. They were going to hide out in a small tributary of the Bobonaza a little way upstream. They waved and went on.

When I asked Severo why they did not stay behind to fight their enemies, he spat into the water.

"They are civilized," he said, "and no longer warriors."

He spat again. "Also," he said, "they are wise. They do not wish to have their heads shrunk."

A few minutes later we passed a second dugout in which were two white traders furiously paddling in the opposite direction.

One of them, a squint-eyed little man who wore a huge, walrus-like mustache as if to make up for the total absence of hair on top of his head, melodramatically shouted across to me, "Flee!" His voice squeaked foolishly. "Flee!" he said again.

"Why?" I demanded.

"The Jívaros are on the warpath," he said, "and your head will surely be shrunk." The very fat younger man with him nodded emphatically.

"And yours, too," he said, looking at Severo.

Severo shook his head, his eyes laughing but his mouth in a straight, serious line. "Not this head," he said. "No one will shrink this head. I will die with it on my shoulders."

Although he didn't mention it once during the entire expedition, I later found out that Severo commands all the Jívaro settlements from the Copataza River to the Macuma, an area of several hundred square miles. He is chief of chiefs, both of friend and foe, and he was chosen, as so seldom happens in more complex societies, because he is the strongest as well as the wisest man.

However, even though I didn't know about Severo's position at the time, I wasn't much worried by the warning of the two white traders. I knew I would go as far as I could into Jívaro territory as a friend and, if the wars of revenge became too widespread, I would turn back. Thus I had nothing to worry about.

By the time it began to get dark I once more asked Severo to urge the paddlers to hurry; he did, and they nodded agreeably, then stopped for at least ten minutes to discuss a large green bird which was sitting on the bank of the river. When they were ready they paddled on, and a little after dusk we arrived at Sarayacu, a sad little settlement only five days upriver from the much-disputed Peruvian border.

The first thing we saw was a large, weather-beaten sign on which were written the words, *"El Marañón Es y Será Ecuatoriano"* (The Marañón Is and Will Be Ecuadorean). The letters were carelessly painted and far from a uniform size, but the meaning was clear enough.

The area of the Marañón, the ownership of which has been a subject of bitter dispute between Ecuador and Peru since the earliest colonial times, has since 1949 belonged to Peru, a decision which any even remotely red-blooded Ecuadorean will argue against at any time, often handing out a few black eyes to emphasize his point.

When our dugout drew up to the dock of Sarayacu, the local prefect was waiting for us. He was a tall, gray-haired man with a flaming red face. His shabby, rather grimy shirt was unbuttoned, and his hairy chest had the words *"Ecuador Mi Patria"* (Ecuador My Country) tattooed across it.

As I stepped out of the boat, the prefect, Señor Vitery, leaned forward and roughly grasped my hand in his huge one. He grinned broadly, revealing a row of almost perfect large white teeth.

"Welcome to Sarayacu," he said. "Our hospitality awaits you."

I took his hand, then stepped away and shook myself vigorously. Half a mile back, just after my clothes had dried from the early afternoon rain, the dugout ran through rapids, and I was soaked again.

Señor Vitery hurried me past the small straw huts where the seven soldiers who had the misfortune to be stationed in Sarayacu were living. Five of them were standing in the doorways of the huts, either beside their Indian wives—a word used here only in the loosest sense—or with a brood of solemn dark children at their feet. The other two soldiers, Señor Vitery explained, had only arrived a few days before and thus had not had a chance to decide which of the many Indian girls available they preferred. "However," he grinned, his huge teeth gleaming, "they will choose. They always do." The usual tour of duty, he went on, is from two to three years, but, when the time comes for a transfer, most of the soldiers ask for another hitch.

"Sarayacu gets in their bloodstream," said Señor Vitery, laughing loudly. "They can never escape." He paused for a moment. "I know," he said. "I cannot."

When we arrived at his home, a modest, four-room house built of the cheapest wood, he took me to the second bedroom and insisted that I make myself at home. Then he gave me a ragged pair of trousers and a patched shirt of his in exchange for my wet trousers and khaki shirt.

"You will want a nap," he said, pointing to the narrow cot without a mattress. "I will call you in time for dinner and"—he winked broadly—"a little drink that is not necessarily water."

While I slept I dreamed that I was being attacked by a cannibal fish which, clearly and distinctly, had the same set of teeth as Señor Vitery.

When I wakened I was covered with a cold sweat, and, as Señor Vitery poured the aguardiente out of the bottle, it was quite a long time before I said "when."

The other guest at dinner that evening was a thin, elderly man considerably over six feet tall, with piercing black eyes half-hidden under shaggy, untrimmed brows, a huge, arc-shaped nose, and narrow, humorless lips; he was dressed entirely in black and could easily have passed for an old-fashioned Protestant clergyman.

He swilled aguardiente before, during, and after dinner; he smoked cigars incessantly, one of his own, two of mine, and one belonging to Señor Vitery; he continuously blew smoke in the face of Madame Vitery, a handsome Quechua woman of immense patience; he pinched the bottom of each of Señor Vitery's three daughters as they served us, and he monopolized the entire conversation.

He had theories about everything, including the atomic bomb. He claimed to have panned gold in California, hunted polar bears in Alaska, shot deer in Montana, and twice worked his way around the world as a member of the U. S. Merchant Marine.

After dinner, when the aguardiente was beginning to take hold, he got a little more realistic and confessed that he had been a rubber trader in his youth and later had operated various slightly dishonest games for carnivals and at fairs both in North and South America. As a result, he said, taking a long, filling drink of the aguardiente directly from the bottle, he had spent considerable time in jail.

His longest sentence, he said, reaching over and removing the last cigar from Señor Vitery's shirt pocket, was in Quito. For months he and a partner had successfully counterfeited large sums of money. Then they had been arrested.

"It was a disgrace," he said. "My partner and I were sent to jail when we should have been rewarded. After all, ability is what counts in this world." He paused, blowing a mouthful of smoke in the general direction of Madame Vitery.

"We could counterfeit money while the police and the judge who sentenced us could not. Why be jealous? Why didn't they learn?"

He lifted the aguardiente bottle and drained it. Then he called for another, and when Señor Vitery politely explained that no more was available, he frowned, shrugged, and rose.

"Then there is no more reason for my staying awake," he said, disappearing down the hall.

I am a light sleeper, but the next morning when I woke up, the bottle of Cinzano I had left on the bureau was empty. It had been full when I went to sleep the night before.

However, the tall, ministerial-looking visitor was gone. He was, he had told Señor Vitery, on his way to the Jívaro country to buy shrunken heads.

While I was among the Jívaros I asked about him several times, but no one had heard of him. I often wondered if his own head hadn't perhaps ended in some Jívaro collection; even shrunken, it would have been quite impressive.

After leaving Sarayacu, Severo, Teolo, the porters, and I made a two-day trek by jungle path to a settlement on the Copataza. The first morning, while cautiously picking my way across a bridge consisting of two logs above a turbulent stream, one of the logs fell into the river. I dangled a hundred feet in the air by one leg, until Severo helped me work my way to the other side. A little less than an hour later, as we were crossing a huge, desolate-looking swamp, I slipped from the log path laid across it and in seconds had sunk in quicksand to my waist. Severo and one of the porters were finally able to lift me out.

Travel in the jungle is never dull.

We spent the first night out of doors and at dusk on the second day arrived on the right bank of the Copataza. The clearing was no more than a hundred yards in diameter, and the jungle pressed ominously in on every side. There was not a breath of air, and, as we walked inside the clearing, a dozen leprous-looking men and women walked out of the sagging lean-to which was their home; they were followed by four small children, all looking alarmingly alike. Their bellies were distended, their bodies covered with scabs, their eyes swollen almost shut. Even the three dogs looked sickly, their ribs plainly visible, huge sores showing through their thin, uneven coats.

There was the cloying odor of death in the still air and over all the nauseous smell of putrefying flesh. A baby coughed as we approached; one of the women wearily scratched herself in a too private place; a man noisily blew his nose on the ground, and a second, who looked a little less cadaverous than the others, extended his thin, boneless-looking hand; there was a large running sore in the middle of the palm. I hesitated momentarily, then gave the man my hand and smiled at him. He smiled back.

There were nineteen of us, not including the dogs, in the leaky lean-to that night, by necessity huddled so close together that our bodies touched. Outside the rain beat down incessantly, but there was still no breeze; there was only the sound of laboured breathing, of hacking coughs, and of occasional moans of pain, and there was that indescribable combination of odors.

Toward morning a woman groaned with what seemed to be a combination of pain and terror; after a moment of silence she screamed. Then there was a movement near her, followed by a muffled, gurgling sound, as if someone were being strangled, and more silence.

I never did find out what happened, and I never discovered the reason for the sickness at the settlement or what it was.

Shortly after dawn the porters from Sarayacu were on their way back home, and Severo, Teolo, and I and two paddlers from across the Copataza were in a dugout going toward the Pastaza River, breathing deep of the clean, moist air.

The morning passed slowly, and I tried fishing for a while, but, although the huge fish had never seen any of Abercrombie & Fitch's best and most delectable-looking plastic baits before, I didn't get a single bite. After two hours and six different baits I gave up.

Once I stood up in the dugout and excitedly pointed out what looked like a huge anaconda hanging from the branch of a tree a little ahead, but it was only a vine, and the men laughed good-naturedly at me.

For almost an hour a small black bird followed the dugout, diving into the water and staying under for from five to ten minutes, coming up for air, then repeating the process. If it was searching for fish, it didn't find any.

Toward noon we went ashore for a while, and Severo shot a marimonda monkey but failed to kill it. The wounded animal continued to hang from a branch even though Severo pointed the muzzle of his rifle to the ground, which most Indians believe will cause a wounded beast to drop automatically. We had to leave the monkey there, hoping it would recover.

Just before sunset, we reached the mouth of the Copataza. To the west was the Sanghay volcano, its snow-capped peak reaching 19,000 feet straight up, a thin column of white smoke rising lazily from its crater, then dispersing against the equally white clouds. The Sanghay looked no more than an hour away, but I knew that by jungle trail and river it would have taken a month to reach it. Distances are measured by time rather than miles in the Amazonia.

A few miles further on we moored the dugout just below a tiny, unkempt army post with a thin, nervous corporal in charge. He had thirteen privates in his command, and he reminded me of almost all the corporals I knew in the U. S. Army. He shouted, he ranted, he raved, he waved his arms, he issued orders, and he made a decision a minute. Most of the decisions were wrong. His name was Chacón.

When I told him that I planned to go to the west of the Pastaza, he shook his head emphatically.

"Impossible," he said. "You cannot go on from here. The west is in the very center of the war. You will have to turn back."

I explained that my permits from the police in Quito allowed me to go wherever I wished, and Chacón chuckled and shrugged.

"All right," he said, as if the idea rather pleased him, "if you wish to be killed, you have my permission to be killed. I would not think of standing in your way."

The corporal had no more to say until after supper when I took out my diary and began recording what had happened since leaving Sarayacu. He immediately leapt up, ran to a huge wooden box under his bunk, and pulled out several legal-sized pieces of paper.

"I, too, am a writer," he said eagerly. "I write poetry."

Then, without further comment, he began reading an interminable poem having to do with his love for a girl in Quito and his loneliness for her; several lines ended with anatomical allusions to the girl which, while they did not rhyme, were vivid.

When he had finished, after what seemed hours, he paused dramatically. I hurriedly assured him that the poem combined the best qualities of Edgar Guest and Nick Kenny, both of whom, I assured him, were leading American poets. He was delighted.

At first I felt rather sorry for him, but later in the evening a shapely young mulatto girl began parading up and down the barracks, wearing nothing but a short white slip. After a few hands of cards she and the corporal walked off into the darkness together. I no longer felt sorry for him.

The next morning before dawn seven new porters, Severo, Teolo, and I began the first of what was to be a tortured thirty-two-day march through the jungle. We left before Corporal Chacón returned to the barracks, because I was afraid he might find an excuse to detain us.

By noon we had already hacked new paths, rediscovered old ones, crossed rivers that were neck-deep, sunk in sticky mud to our thighs and beyond, and crossed uncharted swamps that were sometimes sprinkled with nearly indiscernible patches of quicksand.

When I hung my hammock that night I realized that we were already in the Jívaro country and that at any moment we might be mistaken for an enemy raiding party and, before we could identify ourselves, be in the midst of an attack.

146

Actually, when we came across our first Jívaro in midmorning a week later, he was as surprised and, I imagine, as frightened as I was.

Teolo and I were a little ahead of the others, and as we rounded a turn in the trail we almost collided with the Jívaro. He was a tall, thin man with the muscular grace of a ballet dancer; his strong yet delicate-featured face was painted black; his long, thick hair fell carelessly over his shoulders, and he was wearing a striped, wrap-around skirt.

He stopped, brandished his long, sharp spear at us, and shouted several words which neither Teolo nor I could understand.

I smiled, rather wanly, I'm afraid, and pointed behind us, indicating that others were following us up the trail. My gesture hinted that an entire army was behind us.

The Jívaro grunted, then stepped across the path and waited, staring intently at us.

A few minutes later Severo appeared, and the Jívaro shouted at him. This time I could tell he was angry, and I half turned away, but Severo shouted back, equally loudly and equally angrily, in Jívaro.

The Jívaro listened and finally nodded and turned, indicating that we should follow him. After about half an hour we arrived at a large, circular palisade, and our guide took us to a door that could only have been seen by those who knew its location. It consisted of a single, roughhewn log which the Jívaro lifted to one side, leaving an opening just wide enough for us to squeeze through sideways.

Inside the palisade were two large huts built so close together that their roofs almost touched. They were egg-shaped, perhaps thirty yards long and eighteen yards wide. The conical roofs were made of palm leaves closely woven together and were supported by heavy logs. In the center the cone-shaped roofs were about fifteen feet in height.

Each house had two doors exactly like that in the palisade, one for men, the other for women. When the logs were in place it was impossible to tell their locations.

Our guide led us to the center hut, then indicated that we should wait outside while he entered. A few moments later he returned and gestured for us to follow him into the hut, one by one.

Sitting on elaborately carved wooden stools inside were six men who silently stared at us. They were all powerfully built, and each had a weapon; two had ancient, muzzle-loading rifles of about the 1902 variety which were undoubtedly relics of the rubber boom; the other four had long, uncomfortably sharp-looking lances.

Some had their faces painted red with achote, others black with *huito*. Around their waists they wore heavy skirts of colorfully striped cloth reaching almost to their ankles. Later I found out that the cloth, called *pampallina*, is woven by the men themselves on vertical looms.

One man, who sat a little away from the others, had pinned his hair back and up with an elaborate, comblike feather adornment of half a dozen colors. He looked first at me, then at Teolo and Severo, and finally at the porters, but he still said nothing.

At last Severo seated himself on a long tree trunk in front of the six stools, and he motioned for the rest of us to do the same. As the silence continued I looked curiously around the hut. There were low wooden platforms on every side; I later learned these served as beds. Each was about three feet off the ground, about six feet long and four wide. They were supported by sticks driven into the ground and were rough and unfinished on top.

The Jívaros are practically the only Amazonian Indians I know who don't sleep in hammocks, perhaps because, since they are constantly at war, they have found it's easier to slide off a shelf than to work their way out of a hammock.

To the rear of the hut were a dozen or more silent women making chicha, their long brown robes pinned over their right shoulders, their left shoulders bare. They also wore short, round sticks in each of their ears and a smaller stick through a hole under their lower lips. They continued with their work and seemed not to notice us.

The silence went on for a little more than fifteen minutes; then the chief, the one with feathers in his hair, quietly picked up his stool and placed it squarely in front of Severo. Without looking at him the chief began speaking, softly at first, his voice gradually rising to a shout.

Severo answered in the same manner. Every few sentences each would place the middle and index finger of his right hand to his lips and spit through the opening.

As their voices grew more intense and the spitting more frequent, it sounded as if they were in the midst of a fierce argument; actually they were only exchanging friendly greetings. The Jívaro language is always loud, violent, and emphatic.

After his conversation with the chief Severo turned and talked individually to each of the other five men. Then the chief placed his stool in front of one of the porters; I found out later that they had met before. The process continued until each man in my party had been greeted by the chief and each had spoken to the other five Jívaros. Teolo and I were excepted because neither of us spoke the language. The business of being greeted took about two hours.

Finally there was a moment of silence, and the women quietly approached, each carrying a bowl filled with chicha.

Each urged us to drink from her bowl, and each of us did. To have refused would have been considered bad manners.

Chicha, like the mañoco of the Desanos, is made from yuca tubers. However, the preparation by the Jívaros is quite different. First, the tubers are cooked; then the women, young and old, healthy and sick, chew the cooked tubers into a mash which they spit into a huge wooden container. Water is added, the mash is allowed to ferment for several days, and chicha is ready to serve.

If in serving, however, a woman notices an unchewed piece of tuber in her bowl, she lifts it out, squeezes it over the bowl, and then thoroughly chews the pulp a second time.

The result could hardly be called appetizing; nevertheless, I drank a swallow from each of the twelve bowls; finally, imitating Severo, I took a small swallow from the last bowl, then, holding it in one hand, moved it to the side, thus indicating that I'd had enough. If I hadn't done that, I would have had to take a taste from each bowl a second time and maybe a third.

That afternoon, after hanging my hammock in the middle of the hut, I walked outside and for the first time noticed eight shallow, obviously new graves in two neat rows under a freshly made lean-to of palm leaves. Six of the graves were of regular size, the other two only half as large.

Later Severo explained that the week before the jivaría in which we were staying had been invaded in a raid led by a rival chieftain named Zacary, whose tribe lived near the Copataza River. The raid had occurred at dawn, as they usually do, and in the fighting which followed six warriors had been killed, as well as the two young sons of Paltazara, the chief who was our host. One of the boys was only eight years old.

Paltazara had, Severo went on, become chief only after the

raid had ended. The previous chief, whom I met for the first time that night, was lying on a shelf in a nearby hut. He had been shot in the arm by one of Zacary's men. The wound had festered, and his arm had swollen to twice its normal size. I was certain that he had blood poisoning and couldn't possibly live long.

However, I was wrong; Paltazara was to die first.

The war between Zacary's men and those under the command of Paltazara was by no means ended; it had, for reasons long since forgotten, been going on for generations, it would probably continue for generations more.

In addition Paltazara now had the deaths of his two sons to avenge. He had already called for reinforcements from a nearby jivaría, and during my second evening in his hut they arrived—ten muscular young men, the oldest about twenty-five, the youngest in his late teens.

The next morning the reinforcements, Paltazara, and a handful of his own men took off for a raid on Zacary's jivaría. They would have a journey of from ten to fifteen days, most of it through the densest part of the jungle, always through completely uncharted territory, never over even the roughest trail. On the march the Jívaros are like animals stalking their prey; they invariably attack at dawn; they rely entirely on surprise; the battles last only a few minutes, and there is only one rule: Kill or be killed.

I was invited, but politely declined to accompany Paltazara's army. As a novice, I would have been courting almost certain death on such an expedition.

Instead, Severo, Teolo, and six porters from among those of Paltazara's men who were either too young or too old to fight left the jivaría late the same afternoon. By nightfall we had arrived at another fortified palisade on the banks of the Pastaza. Here we spent the night, and, since he was afraid some or all of the porters would sneak away in the darkness, Severo kept watch.

Thus the next morning our party was still intact. Since the Pastaza along one stretch was remarkably calm, we had no difficulty in crossing, but several trips were necessary in the tiny dugout to get both the men and all our supplies on the other side.

A little after noon we started west through the jungle again and a few hours further on came to the bank of a shallow tributary of the Pastaza. A little way beyond was a narrow trail so carefully hidden by the branches of an overhanging tree that only a Jívaro could have found it. Near the beginning of the trail was a tiny lean-to. By sitting very close together two men could squeeze under the roof.

Severo explained that the night before an attack the warring Jívaros would come, two by two, to the shelter or one like it, and spend several hours drinking maicua, a narcotic which they believe makes it possible for them to speak with Iwanch, the god of the jungle, who tells them the outcome of the forthcoming battle. If they drink enough maicua, Severo said, the prediction is always favorable.

Although no one has ever seen him, the Jívaros believe that Iwanch sometimes appears in tangible form and slithers through the jungle, leaving behind one human and one jaguar track. There is also a god of the river who occasionally disguises himself as an anaconda, frequently as a tapir, and once in a while as a frog. If he wishes, he can, in any guise, bring on destructive floods, beneficial rains, or disastrous droughts.

After leaving the lean-to we went on to the jivaría of a chief named Ayuli; it had been recommended by Paltazara as our stopping-off place for the second night of our journey. However, the jivaría was deserted. The entire population had departed when Ayuli died only a few days before.

As is the custom when a chief dies, his body had been placed inside the hollow trunk of a tree which was then sealed at both ends with a vegetable tar. After that the jivaría was abandoned, with only a daily visit from an old woman who for several months would place food just outside the tree trunk, and when she decided—just how I never knew—that Ayuli's spirit had fled, she would join the others in the new jivaría.

We started off again just before dawn the following morning and days later had reached the jivaría of Chacallema, a broadshouldered man in his late forties who had the face of an amiable pig and a voice like the croak of a laryngitic frog.

He was not happy to see us since we were now in the heart of the warring territory and his jivaría might at any moment be the scene of a battle. He did not want to have his tactics encumbered by the presence of an inexperienced *Apache* (white man). Thus we were permitted to stay overnight, but the first thing the next morning were urged to get on with our journey.

However, since we were all exhausted, Severo used a handful of my cigars as bribes, and Chacallema grudgingly agreed to let us stay several days in the area.

One evening the ten young warriors who had come to Paltazara's jivaría the night before we left arrived at Chacallema's. They were in high spirits, laughing and shouting at each other and explaining their exploits to Chacallema, who listened and occasionally nodded solemnly but never took his eyes off me.

Finally the young fighters seemed for the first time to notice me; they looked first at Chacallema, next at Severo, then, and for a much longer time, at me. After that I heard the word "Apache" repeated several times with a rising crescendo of voices. For a time Severo said nothing; then he began talking loud and fast and, I hoped, convincingly.

There was a moment of silence, but when the laughing began again I realized I was safe.

A few minutes later Severo lumbered over to the darkened corner where I was sitting and explained that the young warriors had been suspicious of me, questioning whether it was safe to allow me to witness the highly secret head-shrinking process they were about to begin. He had done his best to persuade them, he said, and, oddly enough, at the last moment Chacallema had surprised him by agreeing.

As a result, said Severo, I was about to see what few white men have, the shrinking of a human head.

A few minutes later one of the warriors went outside and returned with a small, leaf-wrapped package. He seated himself on the ground, unfolded the leaves, and took out a blood-spattered head from which the skull had been removed.

It was the head of Yauri, the young son of Zacary.

Later I learned that Paltazara's party had arrived at Zacary's jivaría just before sunup two days earlier. Since they knew the territory and we had circled, they traveled much faster than we could. In the brief battle which followed Yauri had been the only casualty. The attackers had hurriedly cut off his head at the base, disappearing with it into the jungle.

As soon as they felt safe from counterattack, they made a cut from the top of the head to the base of the skull, skillfully separating the skin from the bones. Next they discarded the skull and carefully sewed shut the slit as well as the lips and the eye apertures.

Then they wrapped the skin in leaves and started for Chacallema's.

That evening while I watched Yauri's head became a *tsantsa*.

First, the skin and hair were immersed in a clay pot filled with river water and some herbs; after that the pot was placed on a hot fire and left until the water boiled. At the same time sand and pebbles were being heated in other pots.

When the skin was removed from the now greasy yellow water, it had already shrunk a little, and it was allowed to dry partially overnight. The following day hot sand was poured in, left for some minutes, then poured out. This process was repeated three times. Each time the features of the face were painstakingly pressed into shape with a smooth hot stone, and each time the skin became smaller.

Next, half a dozen smooth, hot stones were dropped in, shaken around, and the features again pressed into shape. By this time the skin was no larger than a good-sized apple or orange. Finally a single large stone was placed inside, rolled around, removed, and the skin placed over the fire and smoked until it was black and hardened into shape.

The prized trophy was taken outside and hidden, after which the warriors lay down and immediately fell asleep.

I went out into the fresh night air and vomited.

Our next stop was at Sando's jivaría.

When we entered he was seated in the middle of the huge hut, which was at least thirty yards long and twenty wide. Sando regally gestured for us to wait, and proceeded to paint his face with a red stick. Then, with immense dignity, he moved his stool in front of the porter he knew best. They shouted at each other for a few moments, after which Sando greeted the rest of us, one by one. His manner was that of a medieval king granting an audience to his serfs.

The greetings over, we each had considerably more than our

fill of chicha, and Sando, a huge, muscular man in his mid-forties, came over to me and politely indicated that he wanted to borrow my pistol.

I handed it to him, and he held it at his waist for a moment, then drew it quickly and fired a few imaginary shots at a nonexistent enemy, meantime making a gesture of pleasure by placing his tongue against his palate and removing it quickly; the resulting sound was like the uncorking of a bottle of champagne.

Dinner that evening was served by Sando's four wives, all of them at least twenty years younger than he.

When he had finished eating he filled his mouth with water several times, squirted it on his hands, and wiped them on his skirt. The wives grinned with delight and giggled happily among themselves.

Because they are constantly at war with each other, polygamy is necessary for the survival of the Jívaros. The closest male relative of a man killed in battle or dying a natural death automatically takes over both the wife and the children of the deceased. This is easy because no marriage ceremony is necessary.

If a young man wants a particular girl, he simply mentions it to her father, who tells him to go ahead and take her off his hands. Should the girl have sisters, they go along too, and are also considered married to the young man. In one instance at Sando's a seven-year-old girl was referred to as one of the wives of a warrior. When through Severo I asked Sando if the warrior had intercourse with her, the chief shook his head. No, he said, she was too young; she would not, he added, be able to have intercourse for at least two years and possibly three. Meantime, however, he added, she was being trained in more subtle ways of giving sexual pleasure to men.

Occasionally a second Jívaro decides he wants one of the sisters of the already married woman, and he asks her husband, who again almost never refuses permission because he can always find a replacement. Romance is unknown among the Jívaros, and love is unnecessary.

When, as so rarely happens, a girl is unlucky enough to have a baby before she has a husband, she is treated as a prostitute and anyone can have intercourse with her.

However, unlike those Indians who offer their women to the most casual visitor, the Jívaro women, even the most depraved, are forbidden to have sexual relations with white men. If they are caught, both they and their partners lose their heads. Should a white man be foolish enough to attempt to seduce a Jívaro, she would immediately tell her husband or father, and the man would be killed. If she does succumb and the man escapes, she may, even after her sin is known, be allowed to live, but she is for the rest of her life treated as an outcast. In one jivaría at which I stayed a woman who had had relations with a trader was, during every drunken celebration, tortured by having pepper rubbed into her eyes and rectum.

We spent six days and nights at Sando's, and since there was constant danger of an unexpected attack I always slept with my pistol at my side.

Our original porters, along with the young warriors, returned to the Pastaza, and we had a good deal of trouble finding replacements. However, Severo finally recruited six, after personally guaranteeing their safe return, but just as we were ready to leave the wife of one gave birth to a screaming, red-faced son. In order to protect his son, her husband was forbidden to do any work for three days; so we waited.

On the first afternoon of our renewed journey we saw a tiny dilapidated hut alone in the middle of the jungle. The roof sagged ominously, and the palm-log door was half unhinged; at first we thought the hut was deserted. Then, as we came nearer, a nearly naked old man ran outside.

Immediately the porters screamed and scattered. I could see why. The old man's face was half eaten away, as if by leprosy, and where his nose had once been was only a gaping hole. I've seen dozens of similar cases in the jungle but none quite so far advanced. Severo said that a worm had entered one of the openings of the old man's body, possibly through his nose or ears and, once inside his body, had begun multiplying and eating away the flesh. I imagine the old man could have been saved by treatment, but the nearest doctor was at least several hundred miles away. So there was nothing for him to do but wait to die. Food brought from the nearest jivaría was left daily a hundred feet or so from his hut, but no one spoke to him. No one ever would. After his death the hut would be burned.

Severo and I shouted a greeting at the old man, but he came no closer than fifty feet, mumbled something incomprehensible, turned, and walked back into his hut.

He stood for a moment in the door, watching us sadly, and, as we passed, slowly closed it behind him.

We trudged on, the porters often lagging behind, afraid that at any moment we would meet up with an enemy raiding party. At the time, however, our only foe was the terrain. After we had waded across the then-narrow waters of the Macuma River, we climbed almost straight up for two hours, then made an equally steep descent for another two. At the foot of the mountains we again met up with the Macuma, which turned on itself a few

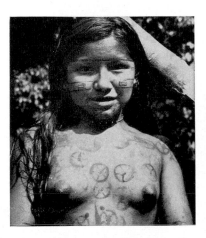

Jívaros *Above,* A Quechua Indian girl decorated with dyes obtained from jungle plants. *Right,* Severo Vargas and two Quechua Indians from the Bobonaza River. *Below,* The author and a Jívaro hut of the Macuma River area

Jívaros *Above,* The crossing of the Chiguaza-Tuna River in Jívaro country. *Below,* Chief Paltazara and one of his warriors

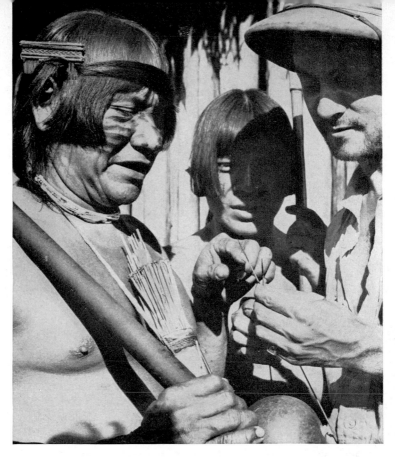

aros   *Above,* Chief Sando explains poisoned blowgun darts.
ow left, Chief Yungara and one of his men. *Below right,*
nbekete and the *tsantsa* of Yauri

Jívaros   *Above*, A marimba made by the Negroes of the Pacific coast and brought by the Cayapas. *Below left*, Borbón, a village on the Cayapas River. *Below right*, Cayapa girl and a Cayapa girl and her jungle rat, a pet

Jívaros *Above*, A Cayapa Indian girl and the author. *Center*, On the way to Tumaco. *Below*, The falls of Inés María at Baños, Pastaza River

Vaupés *Above*, The main *maloca* at Tipiaca. *Top right*, A *batelo* on the Vaupés River. *Center right*, Pedro Pablo and the author. *Below right*, Lui, a Desano Indian girl of the Vaupés River

Vaupés *Left,* After climbing Muj-Tuke a Kubeo Indian points toward Tipiaca. *Center,* Kubeo Indians of Tipiaca ready for a *cachirí. Below,* A Macú Indian of the Vaupés preparing coca

Vaupés *Above,* A typical trader's house on the Vaupés. *Below,* A fish trap across the Abiyu River

Orinoco *Above*, The Orinoco River with Duida mountain in the far distance. *Below left*, The dance at Capihuara. *Below right*, The author

Orinoco *Above,* The heavily loaded boat on our way up the Orinoco River. *Right,* Teolo digging for turtle eggs, Duida mountain in back. *Below,* We make a stop to load up on turtle eggs

Orinoco   *Above*, Duida mountain at Esmeralda. *Below*, Getting
ready for the departure after a night spent on the beach

Orinoco The first Guaica Indian settles down next to Severo

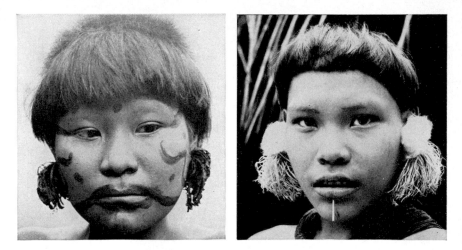

Orinoco *Above left,* A Guaica woman. *Above right,* A Guaica beauty. *Below,* The lean-tos around the clearing of Mahakodo-Tedi

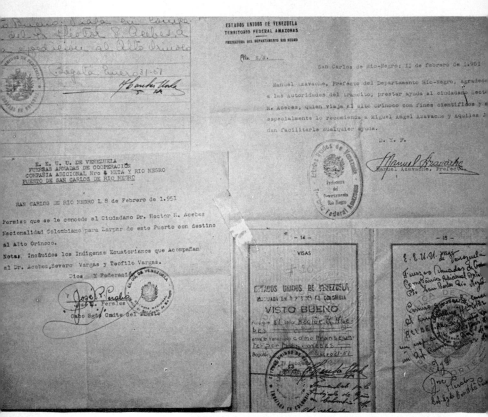

Orinoco *Above,* The official documents given to me by the Venezuelan authorities to carry out the expedition. *Right,* Guaica bows

Colorados *Left,* A social gathering. *Above,* A Colorado Indian

Leticia *Right,* The smallest Amazonian monkey

Llanos *Left*, Crossing Quebrada Honda in the Serranía de la Macarena. *Center*, La Macarena in background. *Below*, Serranía de la Manacacias

miles further up and circled around, completely enclosing the narrow chain of hills.

The river at this point was twice as wide and considerably deeper than at the spot at which we had originally crossed; thus, to avoid being swept away by the current, we locked hands as we crossed the hundred-foot width, the angry swirling waters beating hard against our chests.

A few minutes later we arrived at Uyungara's fortress, which was barricaded not by one but two rows of poles, and it took half an hour of argument on Severo's part for us to get inside. Then we met Uyungara himself, a man of towering strength with the dark, angry face of an English bull and the shoulders of an aging halfback. He was surrounded by a dozen of the most muscular and fierce-looking warriors I have ever seen. I could understand then why the Jívaros have never been subdued, not even by the Incas, and why, for that matter, they probably never will be.

Since Uyungara was expecting an attack at any moment, none of us got much sleep that night. Nothing happened, but the next morning, shortly after sunup, we started on the last lap of our trip. Our destination was Ambusha's jivaría, where Yauri's tsantsa now was. Ambusha's two sons, Romo and Hembekete, had taken part in the raid on Zacary and were part owners of the shrunken head. The Jívaro who fells a man is, logically, considered the first owner of the head, but if a second merely jabs at the prostrate enemy with his lance, he is thought of as the second owner, and so on down the line of those who participated in the successful raid.

Beginning a few months thereafter, each owner holds a separate victory celebration, and when we arrived at Ambusha's jivaría preparations for the first had just begun.

The jivaría had been lengthened by at least twenty feet; additional platform beds had been placed all around the walls, and, although it would be some time before the actual celebration, huge quantities of barbasco were being made for poisoning fish, hunting parties were being organized to collect meat, and all of the women were busy making gallons of chicha.

When Severo told Ambusha that, if possible, I wanted to see a sample of what the actual celebration would be like, the old chief's face broke into a childish grin. He nodded happily and passed the word along.

Ambusha was a foolish-looking man of perhaps fifty-five. He had a fat face, thick lips, and a wide nose across which freckles spread crazily. His hair was a bright red. He was also the most talkative Indian I've ever come across, and he seemed to have been waiting for the chance to plan an extra celebration. Later I noticed that he managed to get down at least twice as many drinks of chicha as any of his followers.

The festivities began at dusk, with the macabre tsantsa hung from a lance which was stuck into the ground in the middle of the hut. The tiny, evil-looking head swayed gently and seemed to change expression in the light of the flickering fires, sometimes appearing to grin, again to frown ominously at the perspiring Jívaros dancing around it.

In a few minutes the entire party had forgotten that this was only a rehearsal for the real event. Only a few swallows of the fermented chicha were necessary to produce drunkenness. Both the men and the women circled the swinging head, first clockwise, then counterclockwise, the shell belts and bone anklets of the women rattling rhythmically as they stamped their feet in the dry earth.

Then, without warning, the large circle broke into three smaller ones, and the shouting began, words that sounded like "*Congupe, congupe, congupe*," these repeated for perhaps five minutes, then changing into something like "*Yambuna hay, yambuna hay, yambuna hay,*" and finally, "*Chacua hay, chacua hay, chacua hay.*" Intermittently the dancers would stop for a round of chicha, after which the shouting and dancing would begin again. There was sex throughout the night. Sometimes the men disappeared into the shadows with their wives, more often with someone else's. Nobody seemed to care; nobody appeared to notice.

At dawn everybody fell drunkenly into his or her or somebody else's bed platform, and most of them did not awaken until dusk, and then the dancing and drinking and sex began again.

That night I was so tired I merely lay on my hammock in the center of the hut, watching listlessly.

The actual celebration would take three days and nights, and I was just as glad that I would miss it. On the morning of the third day we said our good-bys to the bleary-eyed Ambusha and started north.

Early in the afternoon we arrived at the forlorn, unpainted hut of one of the few white men living in Jívaro territory.

As we approached, Señor Juan Bravo rushed out to greet us. He was a tall, wiry yuca farmer of about fifty with a thick head of gray hair, most of which stood straight up, as if to emphasize the appropriateness of his name, which in English means "angry." He was barefoot, and his rough clothes hung loosely on his emaciated frame.

He smiled broadly when he saw us and extended his grimy, work-calloused hand. "Welcome," he said formally, "welcome from Señor Juan Bravo."

He ushered us into his tiny hut, which was nearly bare of furniture but meticulously neat. Since I was wet from recently crossing a stream, I first changed my clothes in front of the roaring fire of the old-fashioned stove in the kitchen and then sat down to a cup of *huayusa* which Señor Bravo had sugared heavily. Huayusa is made by steeping leaves in boiling water and, unsweetened, is so bitter that it causes immediate vomiting. Thus the Jívaros frequently use it to cleanse their stomachs after a night of heavy drinking.

However, with sugar the drink tasted rather like a strong tea, and, while listening to Señor Bravo's almost uninterrupted monologue, I sipped from the steaming cup, nodding at appropriate intervals.

The señor, who had lived in the same shabby hut for thirteen years, had grown to admire the Jívaros, particularly the simplicity of their religion. At one time, he said, they had worshiped the sun, the moon, and the nearby volcanoes, believing that earthquakes and all other natural calamities were caused by one or all of these divinities when angered.

Now, however, he went on, they believe that a single supernatural being created the first Jívaro in the form of a sloth. They call their god Tsaratuma, and when they capture a sloth they hold a feast in celebration, after which they kill the sloth. They are convinced that in so doing they increase the wisdom and virtue of all those who partake of the meat.

On the other hand they believe that the deer is the devil, and they will not eat deer meat for fear of having horns grow on their heads.

When Señor Bravo paused for breath, it was midafternoon, and I decided that we ought to try to reach the next jivaría by sunset.

The señor was heartbroken. "But, no," he said, "you cannot leave. You have only arrived, and I have not seen a white man for nearly a year."

Nevertheless, I shook Bravo's hand and, without looking back, started off into the jungle again.

A few minutes later one of the porters who was walking a little ahead of the others neatly deposited his load by the side of the trail and quietly disappeared. I found that a few hours before a thorn had become enmeshed in his foot, causing it to swell painfully. Instead of asking for treatment he had preferred to take off by himself, making the painful, week-long journey back to his own jivaría alone.

His load was distributed among the other porters, and we went on, reaching Ananga's jivaría shortly after dark. We were told that night that a few days earlier one of the young warriors had gone off into the jungle to collect barbasco for poisoning fish. He did not return by nightfall, and the next morning his body was discovered a few hundred yards away. As so rarely happens in the Amazon jungles, he had come across a jaguar which, instead of running, had attacked him. All around were the signs of a fierce struggle, but the man's torso was intact.

The head, however, had been torn from the body, and the signs of a bloody feast remained.

After leaving Ananga's the trail widened perceptibly, the result of an intermittent flow of foot traffic between two lethargic, isolated settlements, Macas and Arapicos, each with a population of fewer than a hundred whites.

A few minutes after we started it began pouring rain, and since the ground was already soft we were soon knee-deep in mud. We went forward slowly, and twice I fell on my face, smearing my whole body with the thick, oozy mud.

A little later, while edging my way across a fallen tree trunk over a narrow river, my boots slipped on the slimy surface, and I was catapulted into the roaring waters below.

Since I was soaking wet before falling, I emerged not much

wetter but considerably cleaner than before. A few seconds earlier Severo had shouted, "Careful, Señor Acebes."

I had disdainfully waved him aside. "Careful yourself, Severo," I had said.

The cold sheets of rain continued to drench us, but we went on, the guides stopping every few minutes to shake themselves, mumbling complaints, partly directed at the sky, partly at me.

Then, without warning, we came to an abandoned shelter, which consisted of a loosely woven thatched roof without side walls. We shivered inside until the rain stopped temporarily and the blazing sun emerged once more.

I finished my cigar and nodded to Severo. "Let's go," I said.

He shouted at the men, but they shook their heads angrily and shouted back. The argument continued for several minutes, and then Severo said, "They want to stay here all night. They say we have two more rivers to cross and the water will be too high for us."

"Well?" I asked.

"Well," said Severo, shrugging his shoulders, unwilling to make the decision.

I paused for a moment. It had been raining for at least three hours, and in the jungles of the Amazon streams often change their levels as much as five or six feet after only a few hours of rain. As a result I have often had to wait for an entire day for the water to subside in a stream that normally could be waded across.

In addition there is always the problem of the current. Some rivers can be waded if they are chest deep; in others the current is so strong that they cannot be crossed if the water comes above the knees. What's more, it is best to ford a stream where the waters are not perfectly calm, to lessen the chances of an attack by piranhas and caimanes. Thus it is always best to let the guides decide on the spot to cross. They know the rivers both by instinct and from generations of experience.

In this case, however, I decided we ought to continue. We were in the midst of the rainy season, and by the next morning the water, instead of being lower, might have deepened.

So I motioned our party on.

From the bank the waters of the Chiguaza-Tuna seemed ominously high, but Severo, after a careful survey, nodded, and we started across together, holding on to each other. The water was nearly up to my neck. As we neared the opposite shore the intensity of the current increased, and we were nearly struck by a swirling tree trunk almost two feet wide and nine feet long. If the trunk had hit us, we would both have been knocked out and immediately dragged under by the current, but fortunately the huge piece of wood raced by, missing Severo's head by no more than an inch or two.

From the opposite bank of the Palora River, about three quarters of a mile away, the lazy little settlement of Arapicos looked calm and cool and civilized. I was so delighted to be there that I took out my pistol and fired two quick shots into the air.

There was no reply. It was siesta time, and Arapicos slept on. At the place we stopped the waters of the Palora were low, and brief stretches of sandy beach as well as huge, round boulders were dry and naked all the way across. In between, however, the current rushed angrily and noisily.

From the top of the bank to the bed of the river was a dull, slate-colored cliff at least thirty yards straight down, and we descended hand over hand by means of a liana ladder. Then, jumping when possible from one stretch of sand or one rock to another, we began to make our way across the river, holding hands when we came to those spots where the current was swiftest. It took us a little more than an hour and a half to get from one side to the other.

Finally we climbed up another liana ladder and were in Arapicos.

There were only twelve shacks, all small, all unpainted, most of them in need of drastic repair.

There were also thirty-five inhabitants, the most beautiful of whom stood in the doorway of the largest shack waving to us. She was the young wife of Señor Jerónimo Jaramillo, prefect of the town as well as its richest inhabitant. He has a twelve-acre farm and three cows. His wife would be considered attractive anywhere.

Jaramillo was in Macas, but the señora made us welcome. Within a few minutes after our arrival I was drinking a glass of fresh milk and wolfing down a steak served on a porcelain plate by clean hands.

What's more, shortly after eating, I fell into a real bed for the first time in weeks and didn't wake up until fourteen hours later.

By that time Señor Jaramillo had returned. He was a good-looking man in his mid-thirties with a hard, muscular body, a shy smile, and soft brown eyes.

He was delighted to have guests and in the afternoon pointed out the virtues of his little farm and the three rather emaciated cows.

That evening he invited in four of the settlement's leading citizens, including the pale, aesthetic-looking young schoolteacher.

He was not more than twenty, and he had probably not had more than four or five years of schooling himself, some reading and writing, a little arithmetic, a great deal of religion, and, perhaps, some geography. Nevertheless he was a civilized young man, observant, witty, and intelligent.

What's more, he talked almost incessantly, and he was an excellent raconteur. One of his stories was about a handsome, bearded missionary who a few years before had been working among the Jívaros.

The Indians immediately fell in love with his head, mainly because of his long, luxuriant beard, the first they had ever seen. Naturally they wanted the tsantsa of it.

However, since the missionary had talked a great deal about some kind of god who seemed to be in charge of everything, they decided that they should not kill him without getting the god's permission. So they secretly chose half a dozen representatives to make the long journey to the mission from which the bearded priest had come.

When the six Jívaros arrived at the mission, they asked for the god, and the abbot emerged. Then they handed him a slip of paper on which somewhere along the way a literate man with a sense of humor had written the following:

"Dear god, will you be good enough to give us permission to cut off the head of the missionary, Pedro Mendes. It is a head very much admired by all of us, and we desire to make it into a tsantsa."

"Naturally," said the teacher, laughing, "the abbot had to refuse, but he did so reluctantly. If he had said yes, the entire Jívaro population might have been converted to Christianity."

It was late when the party broke up, and just before he left the thin-faced young teacher took my hand in his and held it for a moment.

"I wish you were not leaving," he said.

I nodded. "I wish I weren't either," I said. "But, you know . . ." I paused.

"You cannot understand," he said. Then came a line which has already been and will continue to be spoken thousands of times by thin-faced young men in small towns and villages over the world.

"Here," he said, "there is nobody to talk to."

Early the next afternoon, Teolo, Severo, and I got considerably ahead of the porters. We were in the densest part of the jungle. The giant trees grew no more than a few feet from each other, so close that almost no sunlight came through.

Nevertheless, we stumbled ahead, working our way over hundreds of fallen logs, taking each step deliberately to avoid becoming entangled by the trailing vines that were everywhere underfoot.

In addition a cold rain was falling, and all three of us had several times slipped shoulder-deep into the mud.

By evening we had reached the banks of the Llushin River, and we sat down on the floor of a filthy abandoned hut nearby to wait for the porters to catch up with us.

They never did; instead, along with all of our equipment, they spent the night comfortably in a sturdy, walled shelter we had passed several hours before.

Meantime, shortly after dark, Severo, Teolo, and I built a huge fire and dried our clothes. After that, supperless and still caked with mud, we lay down on the littered floor of the hut, tried to ignore the thousands of insects, and pretended to sleep.

Shortly before dawn, when I did actually doze off, I was attacked by at least one vampire bat and God knows how many sucking butterflies.

Probably more foolishness has been written about vampire bats than any other living creatures. They are tiny creatures, never more than two inches long, and, despite all the legends, there is no record of their ever having killed anyone, although they can cause a serious loss of blood. They never attack when you are awake. You can be completely silent and unmoving for minutes at a time. No bat will appear. But the minute you doze, the vampire will light on your toes, finger tips, or nose and begin fluttering its wings so quietly and rapidly that the area attacked is said to be anesthetized. In a few seconds the vampire makes four tiny holes with its teeth and begins lapping up blood. It may drink its fill at one spot or try a second or even a third. Finally it flies away, and for some time thereafter you continue to bleed. Apparently no one ever wakes up while the vampire is at work.

Naturally you may be weakened by the loss of blood, but that is about all.

On the other hand, cattlemen have told me that they are more afraid of the vampire than of marauding wild animals. The bats leave open wounds in cattle in which blowflies deposit their eggs. The screwworm which usually results often kills the cattle.

When I woke up in the morning considerably tireder than when I had gone to bed, I discovered I had only one series of incisions, on the end of one of my big toes. The large, raw sore on my lip had been caused by a sucking butterfly.

When the porters arrived, fresh and rested, I gave them a short but not very effective lecture on their duties, and we started on toward Shell-Mera, a camp established by the Shell Oil Company of Ecuador.

There was no let-up in the rain. We were often knee-deep in mud on the jungle trails, and, when we crossed the numerous rivers, we were usually up to our waists in water.

In addition to being wet through, all of us were bleeding. As we scrambled in and out of the river beds, we tore our hands and faces on the thorn-covered bushes lining the banks.

What was I doing in the jungle?

When the famous mountain climber Paul Mallory was asked why he had so often risked his life in attempt to reach the summit of Mt. Everest, he said, "Because it is there."

The same answer will do for me.

The jungle is there, its giant trees reaching for the sky, their branches and leaves interlaced into a broken roof of green. Everywhere are lianas twisted into bizarre shapes, climbing endlessly along the tree trunks, embracing them like so many thin anacondas, at times almost squeezing the life from the trees.

There are vines overhead, too, their shredded green ends dripping moisture, jumping from tree to tree, fighting for space and for survival.

And always underfoot, their roots extended in every direction like the enormous legs of spiders, are the roots of the trees and plants, some green, some brown, some yellow, some purple, and often the startling red of a flower against the uneven carpet of moss.

There are tiny, crystalline brooks, sometimes murmuring over smooth stones, later becoming part of the raging waters of a river on its way to the ocean, again ending abruptly in a silent swamp.

And, finally, there are the birds, large and small, brilliant and drab, noisy and quiet, sometimes singing, sometimes shouting, always there, surrounded by the thousands of insects, the ants, the mosquitoes, and the many-hued butterflies. And the animals. And the snakes.

The jungle is there all right.

We went on that day on the way to Shell-Mera, and in the late afternoon the rain stopped abruptly. A few seconds later the sun emerged, shining bright against the jewel-like drops on the leaves.

As the sun warmed our skins and began to dry our clothes, the porters broke into an eerie song, and in less than an hour we were at a tiny hut on the banks of the Pastaza.

We were so tired that after a bowl of hot soup each we fell asleep and did not wake until shortly after dawn.

Then we climbed in a dugout and a few minutes later were across the river. An hour and a half after that we arrived in Shell-Mera.

There are four saloons in Shell-Mera, a narrow, muddy main street lined with a handful of shabby, half-empty shops, and a thirty-five-room hotel and general store crowded with cheap merchandise. The latter is owned and run by an amiable Negro from La Esmeralda named Quiñones.

Quiñones, a huge, dark brown man in his mid-thirties, grins at all his customers and guests through a mouthful of gold teeth. He laughs, shakes their hands, sells them drinks, shows them to their rooms, and sees to it that no one ever escapes without paying cash—usually in advance.

The town of Shell-Mera itself has a permanent population of about three hundred, and there are a hundred or so more in the camp across the road.

The town itself is always prosperous, and, when Quiñones returns to La Esmeralda to retire, he will unquestionably be a rich man. When, after four or five months in one of the Shell outposts, the Indians come to Shell-Mera, they are always loaded down with cash.

Their first stop is invariably at Quiñones' store, where they buy a new pair of shoes, a khaki shirt and trousers, and always a bright necktie, which Quiñones himself usually ties for them. After that they never remove the tie until it is worn out, because they are unable to knot it themselves.

With the money left after they are outfitted they step into the nearest bar, and while they are having their first drinks they are accosted by one of the chubby, often diseased Brancas, the local name for the imported prostitutes who sometimes seem to outnumber the permanent residents.

The Brancas get the Indians drunk, lure them into bed, and proceed to relieve them of all the rest of their money.

After one night in Shell-Mera the penniless Indians return to camp and sign on for another four to six months of work in the lonely jungle oil fields. On their next visit to town, the pattern repeats itself.

The rooms in Quiñones' hotel are small, filthy, and populated by spiders. Over my bed there were various penciled signs in which previous guests gave their opinions of the accommodations. Most of them are unprintable, but one said, "Pay First to Sleep Bad." It was signed by the name of Quiñones, but was an obvious forgery.

However, the sentiment was valid enough. I spent the first hour trying to kill all the black and white spiders in sight, but for every one I squashed, another dozen appeared from under the cracks.

I finally gave up and wrapped myself as tight as possible in my blankets.

When I reached out to turn off my flashlight, I saw one white spider about six inches above my head calmly sucking the life out of a huge cockroach. I quickly turned off the light.

The bite of the white spider produces a fever which lasts

twenty-four hours; that of the black endures for three miserable days and nights.

When I got up the next morning, I had a head- and backache and was covered with welts, but fortunately none was a spider bite.

As I checked out of the hotel I mentioned the spider invasion to Quiñones, but he simply smiled happily and shook his head.

"No spider here," he said, "here high-class."

The next morning Teolo and I took the bus to Quito, where I planned to pay him off. Severo returned to his home in El Puyo, about ten miles from Shell-Mera.

Just before Teolo and I boarded the rickety bus, I turned to shake Severo's hand and, as best I could, thank him for his help on the expedition.

However, when I turned, he was halfway down the street, and he did not turn back. Again I had to remind myself that Indians never say good-by. Very few of their languages even have a word for farewell.

The room Teolo and I shared at the Majestic Hotel in Quito was not particularly luxurious, but Teolo had never seen anything like it, and he was particularly impressed with the bathroom. When he saw hot water gushing from the faucet, he chortled with delight.

"Pucha," he said. "Here the water grows already hot."

Then, leaning over to toy with another faucet, he gave himself an impromptu shower while fully clothed.

However, he didn't mind, and while he was drying himself he became engrossed with the bidet.

"And this little tub is for babies in?" he asked.

I nodded. It was easier that way.

173

After dinner in the hotel restaurant that evening Teolo insisted on putting all the uneaten food in his pocket, including half a plate of a soggy pudding I had been unable to finish. He argued that since I had paid for the food it belonged to us.

However, I managed to persuade him that he should leave everything except the bread. Two months later, back in Bogotá, I discovered the maggoty remains in a pocket of the raincoat I had lent him.

The next morning, after I had paid him, Teolo walked down the wind-swept streets of Quito to the bus and boarded it.

I was still standing in front of the hotel when the bus passed on its way to El Puyo. Teolo was staring out of the window, but he did not acknowledge my presence. He looked through me and beyond.

I raised my hand in a half-hearted wave, then lowered it quickly in embarrassment.

I suspected that when I saw them again, no matter how many months or years or even decades had passed, Teolo and Severo would look up and nod casually at me as if we had not parted at all. That was exactly what happened, too, but that was another expedition.

When I left Quito, the journey to the Jívaros was ended.

7

Later, of course, I was glad I'd missed the plane. At the moment I was only angry.

I glared at the fat man behind the counter in the air lines office in Leticia.

"How long before there's another plane?" I demanded.

"Not long," he said, removing from his mouth the bent pin he had been using as a toothpick. "Only a month."

"You're joking," I shouted.

"No, señor," he said, digging at one of his back teeth with a blackened nail. "There is one plane each month, twelve planes each year, no more, no less."

"How about a boat, then?" I asked.

"A boat," he said, carefully placing the pin in the breast pocket of his sweat-encrusted shirt, "is much simpler. For a boat you will have to wait only ten days."

I stomped out of the office, registered in Leticia's only hotel, the Comisaría, and settled down to wait. The plane to Bogotá had left a little less than twelve hours before, but I was helpless.

Until the paddle wheeler arrived there was nothing to do except make myself at home in Leticia, a forlorn river town at the edge of the jungle with a weary population of fourteen hundred.

I had just returned from a short, eight-week expedition into the Jívaro country, this time on the Upper Marañón, and I was anxious to get home.

But, as I've said, I later realized it was luck that caused me to miss the plane. Except for that particular voyage on the Amazon, I might never have seen Catani again.

Meantime in Leticia I was treated like visiting royalty. Visitors are rare, and I was entertained first by the local government officials, then the officers of the small military outpost, and finally by all of the well-to-do civilians.

I had already been given half a dozen lunches and an equal number of parties, and was exhausted when Fray Miguel de Huarte, the tall, blue-eyed Spanish missionary who had shared with me some of his own encyclopedic knowledge of the region, suggested I attend one of the most bizarre and esoteric rites of the nearby Ticuna Indians.

"You will," he said, "never forget what you have seen."

Shortly before daybreak the next morning half a dozen local civilians, two young army officers, and I started up the Amazon by dugout for the Ticuna village where "La Fiesta de la Moza Nueva" ("The Feast of the New Maiden") was to be held.

When we arrived the preparations were nearly finished. Hundreds of pounds of the meat of wild animals had been roasted; everywhere there were wooden trays piled high with fish, and there were huge vats filled with mazata, a fermented and highly intoxicating drink.

For several nights previously the bark horn had sounded over the jungles, announcing the celebration, and guests from the neighboring settlements had already begun to arrive. They came singly, in families, and by villages, old men supporting themselves by canes, children so young they had to be carried pickaback.

In the afternoon I was given a carefully guided tour and, from a distance, shown the bohío in which was the maiden who was to be the chief attraction at the feast. I leaned close, but was unable to see inside what were really no more than three elliptical cages, each a little larger than the other, like Chinese boxes. Thus it was impossible to see the girl in the smallest cage.

However, I knew she had just reached puberty and had been held there for forty days and forty nights, seeing no one except an old woman who had brought her food and, at the same time, told her of the monsters who would attempt to have intercourse with her during this period of her first menstruation.

The idea was to terrify the girl and later, when I saw her, I could see that the plan had succeeded.

176

The celebration began at dusk.

At a signal from the chief, six young warriors ran from the jungle into the largest bohío of the village, each carrying a huge torch which he placed on one of the half-dozen poles pounded into the ground on every side of the huge elliptical hut.

Then into the flickering, eerie light rushed at least fifty more, men and women, old and young, muscular warriors wearing huge masks of bark cloth, fat old women and voluptuous young ones adorned in feathers of a dozen hues.

Drummers appeared, and the dancers began stamping their feet rhythmically to the beat. Perspiration soon gleamed on their bodies, and dust was suspended in gray clouds everywhere.

Every few seconds a dancer broke the rhythm and squatted for a moment outside the circle while one of the old women brought a bowl of mazata. After downing a few hefty swallows the dancer would once more begin pounding his feet into the bare earth. Less often he would pause briefly to grab a fistful of roast meat or fried fish.

As the dance continued, the grace and rhythm disappeared, and the participants started bumping drunkenly against each other, periodically disappearing into the jungle in pairs.

By dawn there was no one left except myself, three or four drunken hags, and a handful of withered old men snoring soddenly at one end of the hut.

Shortly after sunup I stepped outside the bohío, at which point the only one of the old women who was still sober led the moza nueva out of her prison and into a small, circular fenced-in area. The girl's face was chalky with fear, and, as she scratched herself with a large, roughly carved stick to keep off the monsters she had been told might take away her virginity at any moment, I could see that her hand was trembling.

Then, still trembling and her lips now white with fear, the child was hurried back into her circular prison. After that the three old witches stretched out in front of the hut and went to sleep.

I hung my hammock between two trees and immediately fell asleep.

When I awakened the sun was already disappearing in the west and after my friends from Leticia and I had had some food we gathered near the prison as the *moza nueva* was led out a second time, her eyes now covered with bright blue feathers.

As she was escorted to the center of the largest bohío, which once more was lighted by half a dozen blazing torches, four young women began dancing around her in a gradually expanding circle. Then they seated the girl on the ground and joined the larger circle of dancers.

After that the celebration of the night before was repeated.

At sunrise those few who had not succumbed to the mazata and who had returned from the latest round of fornication lifted the still blindfolded girl onto a large, odorous jaguar hide.

Then the four women reappeared, their eyes bloodshot, moving with the slow deliberation of the half-drunk. They circled her once or twice, after which one of the women reached over, grabbed a heavy strand of the girl's hair and gave a yank.

The girl's lips quivered, but she gave no other sign of the almost unbearable pain she must have felt.

Finally the woman jerked the strand of hair a second time, and it came loose, leaving a bald spot of red pulp on the girl's head. Even then she did not cry out.

A second woman grabbed another strand of hair and repeated the process, then the third and the fourth; next the first woman went to work again. In a few minutes the girl's head was only a bloody mass of red pulp, and the floor was covered with strands of hair to which clung chunks of dripping red flesh.

During the process two of the young army officers from Leticia went outside to be sick, and several times I had to close my eyes and fight down the nausea, but that part of the girl's face which could be seen from under the feathers did not change. Twice she bit her lower lip, then released it slowly.

After the last of the hair had been yanked from her head, the men who were masked threw their disguises on the ground, bent, and lifted the jaguar hide on which she was sitting.

Chanting rhythmically, they carried her to the bank of the river, followed by the older men and the women.

Then the men removed all her clothes, including the feathers over her eyes, lowered her into the river, and took turns bathing her.

Finally they dried her gently, rubbed her still-bleeding scalp with some kind of ointment, dressed her again, and returned her to what was left of her former prison. By this time the outer two layers had been removed.

Here she would wait until a suitor came along. If she were lucky, one might appear immediately. Usually, however, a girl who has been so rudely initiated into maturity has to wait until her scalp heals and her hair beings growing back in again.

Meantime "La Fiesta de la Moza Nueva" continues until the last drop of mazata is gone or there is no one left able to drink.

In this case, shortly before noon, the last two men passed out, and my friends and I retired to our hammocks for an hour or so of sleep before starting back to Leticia.

The entire population of Leticia must have been lining the right bank of the river the morning the paddle wheeler arrived.

As the ancient river boat lumbered toward the pier, its creaking paddle wheel gradually revolving more slowly, Indian boys on-shore shouted undecipherable instructions to the crew. Half-nude Indian girls smiled invitingly at the sailors. Old men waved to those lining the rails of the passenger decks; elderly women anxiously searched the faces, trying to decide which passenger might be begged for a coin or two.

Even the birds seemed to sense the excitement. Hundreds screamed lustily overhead; others briefly lighted on the pier, then flew noisily into the air again.

The paddle wheel groaned to a weary stop, and, in not much less than an hour, the boat was anchored, the bridge lowered, and the officials of Leticia ambled aboard to take a look at the piles of official papers. Most of the passengers strolled ashore.

Nobody hurried. There was plenty of time. The ship would not leave for twenty-four hours.

Meantime I was entertained at another luncheon and that night by the prefect, at whose house I was staying. The party lasted until considerably after midnight, and the next morning I had a slight head. However, I rolled out of bed at a little after sunup and with the help of six porters hurried to my cabin, which was the only one still unoccupied.

As a steward opened the door to show me inside, a huge rat ran for cover.

With the help of the porters I carefully arranged my belongings, placing the clothes I planned to use during the voyage on top of a dusty high table. I left the rest of my belongings in the aluminum drums I use instead of suitcases.

Then I paid off the porters and looked around the steaming box that was to be my home for the eight-day voyage to Manáos. There was dust everywhere; the tiny mirror was cracked, and the porthole could only be opened halfway. The single advantage of my accommodations was the fact that there were two grimy showers nearby.

The heat everywhere was unbearable, and as the whistles blew the boilers groaned, and the huge wheel began turning again I realized that since the broiling sun was beating down on the deck it would be better for me to stay where I was.

Besides, I needed sleep. So I removed all my clothes and lay on the bed to get a few minutes of rest.

When I awakened it was two-thirty, and I was famished.

I called twice through the corridor for the cabin boy, but for a moment there was no answer. Then a deep voice shouted, "Shut up."

I realized then that while I had just awakened from a nap, everybody else was having a siesta.

I called for the cabin boy once more, this time more softly.

In a few minutes he appeared.

When I asked him about lunch he smiled sympathetically.

"I am sorry, señor," he said, "but dinnertime has already passed. However, I can serve you something here."

"What?" I wanted to know.

"Some turtle eggs," he said, "ham, bread, and perhaps even a little butter."

I decided on a ham sandwich and a can of beer, and as the boy went for the food I put on a clean pair of khaki trousers. The heat was still stifling, and I half opened the door to create a draft, then opened one of the drums and took out a tiny gasoline stove, a mess kit I had conveniently forgotten to return to the U. S. Army when I was discharged, and a small can of pork and beans.

As I leaned over to strike a match, there was a knock on the door. Without looking up I said, "Come in."

There was the sound of the door being softly opened.

I turned on the stove, lighted it, and said, still without turning, "Put the sandwich and beer on the table over there."

"But, señor," said a voice, "I have nothing to put on the table."

The voice was that of a young woman, soft and with a real sweetness of quality.

I whirled. Then I dropped the match, cursing. My hand was burned, but nothing could have then been less important.

The girl standing just inside the door was Catani.

Three years had passed since that day when, wearing a bright yellow dress and nothing underneath, Catani had stood on the bank of the Putumayo waving good-by to the Indian boy who had grown up with her on the Meta. She had then already come a long way, but from a settlement on the Putumayo to a river boat on the Amazon is further still, and it is a distance that cannot be measured in miles alone. It is the distance between semi-savagery and civilization.

Catani was a woman now. Her figure was full, neat, and compact, with a hint of voluptuousness. Her dark hair curled loosely about her bronzed face, then fell to her shoulders. She wore no make-up except for a skillfully applied slash of dark red on her rich, full lips. Her unplucked eyebrows curved delicately over her deep, brown eyes, giving her face a constant air of pleased surprise. She was wearing a dress of sheer silk of a pale green color; her legs were bare, and she had on low-heeled, open-toed shoes. Women's legs seldom look right when their owners are wearing low-heeled shoes, but hers did. She had the most perfectly formed legs I have ever seen.

My voice was high-pitched and scarcely recognizable as I asked, "What are you doing here?"

182

She smiled, and I could see that her teeth were white and even.

"I might ask the same question of you," she said.

Then she shrugged. "Traveling," she added.

Since I seemed unable to speak, she went on. "I saw you get on the boat this morning, and I recognized you at once by your green cork hat. I knew you were Ninggi Waycama."

I grinned. The name was one the Indians had given me when I was on the Meta. It means, "The Man Who Travels Alone."

"How did you remember that?" I asked.

"Quite simple," she said. "You were almost the first white man I had ever seen. Besides, on the Meta all of us thought you were crazy."

"Did you think that?" I asked.

"Perhaps," she said.

"And then," I said, "I saw you on the Putumayo."

"Yes," she said, and I had the feeling that she did not wish to pursue the subject.

Fortunately we were interrupted by the cabin boy, who placed the sandwich and beer on the rickety table by my bed and, as I tipped him, winked at me.

As I emptied the beans into the mess kit and began heating them, I motioned for Catani to sit down, and she lowered herself onto the bed, carefully crossing her legs.

I put the next question casually. "Are you traveling alone?" I asked, being sure of the answer.

"No," she said, then added quickly, "I am going to Manáos."

"Wonderful," I said. "So am I."

She nodded, but I could not tell whether or not she was pleased.

We talked while I ate, but I'm afraid I didn't make much sense. I kept wondering what she was doing on the boat, who her traveling companion was, and how many men there had been between him and the young storekeeper on the Putumayo and how many more there would be in the future.

At one point she mentioned that she had been in Iquitos "for a little while." Was it here that she had changed from a half-savage village girl into a sophisticate? At the moment I couldn't ask that or any of the other questions which raced through my mind—who had chosen the perfume she was wearing? Who had picked out the pale green dress? Who had taught her how to apply that skillful dash of lipstick?

In a few minutes she rose, took my hand in hers, and said, "I have now to leave."

I stood up, still holding her hand. "I'm sorry," I said. "When will I see you again?"

She slowly removed her hand. "Soon," she said, then turned and was gone.

I lay back on the bed, the perspiration pouring off my body. After a little while I fell asleep for a second time, smiling to myself.

When I awakened the sun had disappeared, and a cooling breeze was sweeping in through the half-open porthole. I jumped up, took a quick shower, and put on a clean white shirt and my only white suit. The suit had been rolled up in one of the aluminum containers for more than five weeks, and I could not find the cabin boy to press it, but I decided to wear it anyway.

As I looked in the tiny cracked mirror over the filthy washbasin in one corner of my cabin, I could see that I was hardly at my best. In addition to my wrinkled suit my hair badly needed cutting; my nails were long, and even after I had cleaned them each was still circled with unremovable jungle stains.

However, I shrugged and started for the dining room, where four young men even more unkempt than I were making a kind of music on two flutes, a guitar, and a maracas. I picked up a straight-backed chair, ordered a cocktail at the tiny bar, and sat in the shadows on the upper deck until a waiter passed, banging on the dinner gong.

Manuel Leite was already seated at the table for four to which I had been assigned, and as I approached he extended a thin, blue-veined hand, smiled, and introduced himself.

He had perfect teeth, which I was sure could not be his own. His head was half naked and half covered with wisps of thin white hair; his blue eyes were large and clear and rimmed in red, and he had the smile of a cynical child. He was wearing a white, slightly rumpled suit, a stiff white collar, and a tie of deep red that matched the huge ruby in the ring on his right hand.

"Our companions," said Señor Leite, "have not yet appeared, but they are of the female gender, elderly, and unbeautiful. That has always been my experience. The beautiful ones invariably sit at someone else's table."

He was right, too. Our table companions were middle-aged. Both were short, and one was undeniably fat. The other was merely plump. They both had graying hair; their faces were innocent of make-up, and it was not necessary for me to look at their left hands to be sure they were unmarried.

As they seated themselves and began vigorously attacking their food, Leite looked at me and winked.

"You see," he said, "it never fails."

Between bites the thinner of the two women observed that it had been a hot day, and the other said that it was a cool evening. Then the first declared that it would be nice if the days were as cool as the evenings.

"We are on our way to Manáos," said the one who was only plump. I opened my mouth to reply, but closed it quickly. Catani had appeared in the doorway.

She paused for a moment, then walked down the aisle to the only one of the six tables in the first-class dining room which was reserved for two. The conversation at the other tables also died down, and everyone's eyes followed her. She was wearing a short black silk dress, high-heeled black shoes, and her only adornments were a gold pin over her left breast and a thin gold bracelet. She could not have been more beautiful.

On the other hand, the man who seated himself across from her was almost obscenely ugly. He was no more than five feet, three inches tall, and he had a protruding belly, across which was stretched an enormous gold chain. His tiny blue eyes peered through a pair of rimless glasses with enormously thick lenses; his nose was large and liberally pimpled on the end; his chin was lost beneath it, and his sideburns were worn too long, perhaps to make up for his baldness.

However, his white suit was obviously of the finest linen and, in addition to the gold chain, he wore a huge diamond pin on the elaborately flowered blue tie, and there was a second, even larger diamond in a thick gold ring on one of his fingers.

As the waiter obsequiously poured the red wine into her companion's glass, Catani looked up, and her eyes met mine. Then she turned away, giving no sign of recognition.

For the rest of the meal the two spinsters chatted aimlessly about nothing, occasionally glancing with disapproval at Catani. When the waiter brought *tintos* for Leite and myself, they excused themselves.

"They talk too much," said Señor Leite. "Ugly women usually do. Chatter is their shield against their unattractiveness.

"Beautiful women, on the other hand, know that God meant them to be looked at and are suitably silent, leaving conversation for men."

I offered him a Havana, and he sniffed it with satisfaction.

"Such quality is rare," he said. "I have not smoked such a cigar for many months, not since the last time I was in Belém."

As he inhaled the smoke he saw me look again in the direction of Catani, and he smiled appreciatively.

"I see you have taste in women as well as cigars," he said. "A remarkable woman, that one."

I waited for him to continue. Instead he said, "Shall we go on deck?"

I agreed and noisily pushed back my chair. Catani looked up and then away, again without any sign of recognition.

As we passed her table, her companion continued to shovel food into his mouth, a roll of fat bulging out of his collar as he bent closer to the table.

After a turn around the deck Leite and I moved a couple of dilapidated canvas-backed chairs near the rail and seated ourselves. Until considerably after midnight I nodded occasionally while he talked about his lifetime as a rubber trader on the Amazon and its tributaries.

"I have," he said at one point, "been captured one time by the Indians. That was when I was on the upper Xingú—near the spot where the English explorer, Colonel Fawcett, either was ambushed or wandered into an earthly paradise in which there are cities having streets paved with gold. One's theory about Fawcett depends on whether one is a romantic or a realist. For myself, I am a little of both, depending on the occasion.

"This time, however, I was a realist. There were five men in our party, and we had wandered into the jungle beyond our usual

187

depth, when a band of at least fifty natives, all naked and all armed with poisoned arrows, surrounded us.

"We were probably the first white men they had ever seen, and, no doubt, the last. However, they were not charmed by us, and there was no doubt of their intentions. They planned to put us to death. Since none of us spoke their language, there seemed to be nothing to do except to prepare for the inevitable.

"Then, as they were escorting us to their village, and none too gently, I assure you, I removed my false teeth. My mouth was exceedingly dry.

"The chief looked at me with amazement, then he burst into laughter. He shouted for the others to look at the plates I held in my hand. They circled me, and the chief motioned for me to put the teeth back in my head.

"Well, I spent the next week removing and replacing my teeth. My mouth was sore, but I preferred a sore mouth to annihilation, and I performed the operation hundreds of times. Indians came from miles around to look at the miracle, and meantime our party was treated with the utmost courtesy. When I indicated that it was time for us to go, they escorted us back to the edge of the jungle and reluctantly said good-by."

Leite paused and twisted the ruby ring for a moment, then said, "I wish I could tell you that it was quick thinking which made me remove those teeth, but it was only luck.

"Some men are lucky, and some are not."

As he hesitated, Catani and her companion appeared in the shadows at the other end of the deck, looked out over the river for a minute or two, then went back into the dining salon.

"Da Silva, there," said Leite, "is a lucky man."

He rose and stretched.

"Well," he said, "it is time for an old man to retire. Thank you for listening to me. Conversation is my chief indulgence these days. I am too old for romance—and also too poor.

"You, however, are young and not poor. Besides, young men have dreams. Old men know better."

After he left I sat by myself for a while, hoping that Catani would return, this time alone.

At a little after one I went to bed.

Before dinner the next evening Leite and I bribed one of the waiters to bring a small table and two of the dining-room chairs onto the forward deck, and we had been sitting there for a few moments drinking two of the diluted cocktails when Catani's companion, wearing a fresh white suit, this time of silk, came up from below.

Seeing Leite, he walked toward us, smiling and revealing a mouthful of huge yellow teeth stained with tobacco.

Leite introduced us, and the pressure of Da Silva's hand was heavy on mine. Despite the fat belly I could see that in his youth he had been physically strong and, although he was now in his mid-fifties, was still powerful. Leite motioned for another chair, and Da Silva lowered his heavy, squat body into it.

He waved away a drink. "In my youth," he said, "I attempted to drink South America dry. Now I content myself with a glass of good red wine at dinner."

While he and Leite reminisced about a rubber deal they had concluded in Iquitos, I sat in the twilight, sipping my drink and waiting for Catani to appear.

In about half an hour she walked out on deck, this time wearing a dark blue, form-fitting dress and an even larger pin than the one she had worn the night before.

As she approached our table, her face was perfectly calm. We rose, and Da Silva said, "My dear, I want you to meet Señor Acebes."

Catani nodded and smiled, and Da Silva added, "Señora da Silva."

I didn't believe they were married. It was just that fewer questions would be asked if they traveled as husband and wife. At least I hoped that was it.

"How do you do?" said Catani, taking first my hand, then greeting Leite.

"I am," she said, "pleased to meet you."

Another chair was crowded around the small circular table, and Catani seated herself next to Da Silva. While the waiter went for her cocktail, the Brazilian said, "Señor Acebes, here, is an explorer."

"Oh, really," she said, not looking at me. "That must be very interesting."

"Not always," I said, "but I have had one or two fascinating experiences."

It was impossible to tell whether my words had any effect on her. She accepted her drink from the waiter, took a delicate sip, and leaned further back in her chair, looking, except for the alluring brown of her skin, like any of the dozens of smart, well-dressed young women who can be seen any afternoon around five in the better cocktail bars just off Madison Avenue.

Da Silva was insatiably curious about my experiences, and his questions were intelligent. Moreover, as we talked, I forgot his ugliness. He had a charm and urbanity that were, I was certain, the result of a fine education, probably in Europe.

When I asked him, he said yes, he had spent two years at the Sorbonne.

"But that," he went on, "was a long time ago. Now my French

190

is gone; my Spanish is rusty, and my accent is unmistakably Portuguese."

There was only one really bad moment. At one point Da Silva said, "By the way, in your many travels you must surely have explored the Putumayo River. When was that?"

I could see Catani stiffen. Then I shook my head. "No," I said, "I've never been on the Putumayo. That's one for the future, I guess."

After a second of silence Catani turned toward Da Silva and said, "Darling, I am hungry. Could we please eat now?"

He nodded and said, "Of course, my dear, we can do anything you wish."

In the dining room Da Silva insisted that Leite and I sit at his table, and he ordered the best wine—still none too good— and inveigled the waiter into bringing us a fair steak.

The two elderly spinsters who had been left alone looked up at us and glared, and as they left the dining room they sniffed audibly when passing our table.

After dinner Catani excused herself, pleading a headache, and Da Silva, Leite, and I returned to the deck.

It was a good evening. All of us talked a lot, and Da Silva told a good many stories, most of them about one or another of the business deals he had successfully negotiated. He dealt mainly in rubber, but, as he put it, "I have made money in varied activities, some of which I would not now care to discuss."

And he laughed. "A man," he said, "becomes more cautious as he grows older, cautious in business at least, though not necessarily in his personal life."

He looked out at the big river, then back to me. "Now, of course," he said, "I must struggle to keep what earlier I struggled to obtain."

191

As he took my hand after saying good night a little later, he said, "You're all right, Acebes. You're a shrewd man, and I like shrewd men."

After he had gone, Leite smiled through the darkness at me.

"Da Silva does like you," he said, "but I do not believe he is a man who would enjoy being deceived.

"I do not believe he would like that at all."

The next morning the boat stopped briefly near the village of Fonte Boa, and Señor Leite went ashore.

Before leaving he took my hand in his; despite its blue-veined slightness it still had a suggestion of the power he must have had in his youth.

"The old," he said, smiling, "should always avoid advising the young, but, this once, you will forgive me. Be careful, Acebes. With a man like Da Silva and a woman like Catani it is best to be cautious."

Then he paused and laughed. "Of course," he said, "I realize that you will pay not the slightest attention to what I say. When I was your age, I certainly wouldn't have."

He picked up one of his bags, motioned for a porter to take the others, and was gone.

I went below and spent the rest of the day reading in my cabin. Catani and Da Silva did not appear for dinner that evening, but a little later, when I was standing on deck smoking a final cigarette, I heard a slight cough behind me.

I turned. Catani was standing in the shadows.

"It is very beautiful tonight, isn't it?" I said.

She nodded, looked once at the star-crowded sky and the large, full moon, and back again at me.

"Yes," she said, her voice low, almost inaudible. "Tonight it is beautiful."

"Where is your——" I began. I had meant to say, "husband," but decided against it.

"Where is Señor da Silva?" I asked instead.

"He is ill," she said. Her eyes seemed to be intent on something onshore, something deep inside the dark jungle.

"I am sorry," I said.

"Oh," she said, "it is nothing. He suffers often from malaria. This is only another attack."

"How long do these attacks usually last?" I asked.

"Sometimes for days," she said, stepping forward to throw the butt of her cigarette over the side of the boat. As she turned, her arm brushed mine.

As I lighted a second cigarette for her I could see, when the match flared briefly, that her face was white and a little drawn.

"He suffers very much during these attacks," she said. "I must go back to him." She finished only half the cigarette, hurriedly threw it over the side, and excused herself.

"Tomorrow," she said, "it will not be so bad."

I remained on deck for a long time after she had gone, watching the monotonous flow of the sluggish water, glancing occasionally at the moon and the stars, feeling very much alone. At that moment I wished I had not missed the plane.

The next afternoon, while I was sitting on the deck having my usual before-dinner cocktail, Catani appeared and came over to say that Da Silva wanted to see me.

She was silent as she led me down to the darkened cabin where the ugly, now sunken and yellowish face of Da Silva contrasted sharply with the grayish white of the sheet on the bed. He had removed his glasses, and his tiny eyes had almost disappeared in the thick rolls of fat surrounding them, but I could see that despite the fact that he was obviously in pain his eyes were sharp and bright, missing nothing.

He raised the fat hand with the thick diamond ring on one of the fingers and motioned for me to sit down.

"Tonight," he said, "I am hardly in a position to play the host. You must forgive me."

I nodded. "I want you to do me a favor," he said. "It will not be very difficult."

"Of course, Señor da Silva," I said.

"Catani here," he said, "is lonely." He sighed, his usually well-modulated voice just now a monotone. "It is not right for a beautiful young girl to be caged in a tiny cabin smelling strongly of medicines and the odors of an unwashed old man whose body is alternately shaken by fever and chills.

"I want you to take her to dinner with you."

"No," said Catani. "I want to be here with you."

A slight smile crossed his thick lips. "You are kind, Catani," he said. "Whatever else you may or may not be, you are kind. Now go. I shall drink broth, and then I shall sleep.

"I do not want you here."

"Of course, Señor da Silva," I said, "as you wish."

"Please," said Da Silva, "just now I am too sick and too weary for the amenities."

Catani leaned over and kissed him lightly on his forehead, which glistened with sweat. Then we went up to dinner.

After we had finished eating, which we did almost in complete silence, she went back to the cabin. When she returned to the deck, she had thrown a bright red shawl over the black dress—which later in Manáos I discovered was, with the green and blue silk, one of the only three she owned. She had never looked more beautiful, her dark skin gleaming in the moonlight, her lips, which she had made an even brighter red than usual, full and moist, the contours of her figure outlined in silhouette against the side of the ship.

"He is now sleeping," she said as she seated herself in the rickety deck chair beside me. "It is good that he can sleep."

We sat up until long past midnight, and I really can't remember what we talked about. I did not question her about her past or about her relationship with Da Silva, and she did not volunteer any information—except once, just before she said good night.

I had said something about Da Silva's shrewdness and added, "He must be a very rich man."

Catani grinned; it was the first time she had even smiled during the entire evening.

"Very rich," she agreed.

"And he is very fond of you, isn't he?" I went on.

She shrugged, still grinning.

"All this amuses you immensely, doesn't it?" I asked.

"All what?"

"The fact that Da Silva seems to like me. I've watched you when the three of us are together. Your eyes give you away."

"What if I am amused?" she asked, still smiling.

"Well," I said, "I'm just curious. Don't you think you owe him a good deal? And if you deceived him, wouldn't you lose everything?"

She turned away as she replied, but I could see that the smile was gone.

"Look," she said. "I am fond of Da Silva, and I have not deceived him, but, sooner or later, I will lose him anyway. We have been honest with each other. When he tires of me, he will send

195

me away. He has told me so, and I have a feeling that that time is not far off."

There was nothing to say to that.

"Besides," she added, turning again, allowing me to see the tiny drops of moisture in the corners of her eyes, "what is it to you? Da Silva measures everything in money, and he buys what he wants. He wanted me; he bought me. Now he is being kind to you. There is a reason. He has always before been jealous of young men. He was afraid one of them might seduce me."

"Well," I said, "perhaps he thinks I am safe. He may believe I can't possibly seduce you."

Her eyes were suddenly those of the girl I had seen on the Putumayo, childlike, innocent, and, at the same time, savage.

"What do you think, Ninggi Waycama?" she asked.

"I haven't made any passes at you," I said, waiting.

She was silent.

"Have I?"

"No," she said, "not exactly.

"And that," she went on, rising, "may be the trouble."

At noon the next day the boat docked at the port for Manáos.

Just before I went ashore, Catani, who had been on the other side of the deck, apparently arranging for Da Silva to be carried ashore, came over and gave me the name of the hotel at which she and Da Silva were to stay.

"He wants to see you again," she said. "It is as I told you; he has a proposition to make."

I registered at the same hotel, which I'm told is the best in Manáos, and after a bath and a change of clothes went out to take a look at the New York of the Amazon.

Manáos is a thousand miles from the sea, but early in the

196

century great ocean liners from all the ports of the world used to anchor at its docks. The only boats that stop there now are aging river craft like the one on which I'd come, most of which have already had a normal lifetime of service on the Mississippi.

When the rubber boom was at its height, Manáos was its center. It was the world's richest city in per capita wealth—and also the most expensive and widest open. More than sixty-five per cent of all the houses were occupied by prostitutes, girls who had been imported from Paris and London and Madrid and Morocco and who, if they were lucky, were able to return home in a few years, most of them wealthy. I don't know what their fees were, but I'm told that, simply for serving a meal, waitresses got tips averaging $50 each.

Of course many waitresses and prostitutes married the rubber kings. As always in such a society, white women were at a premium.

In addition Manáos was then something of a cultural center. Great actors, singers, and dancers always made at least one visit there—usually for twice and three times the fees that even now are paid entertainers in one of those lush night clubs in, say, Las Vegas. They appeared at what was then the most luxurious, surely the most ornate, and one of the ugliest opera houses in the world. The cost is usually placed at between ten and fifteen million dollars. This was long before the days of prefabrication, but the marble building was put together in England, then taken apart and the pieces shipped across the Atlantic and up the thousand miles of the Amazon to Manáos, where it was reassembled.

It was placed on a hill in the center of the city, topped by a now-tarnished dome tiled in gold, green, and blue, out of which at present grow bushes and even young trees. From a distance it looks rather like a gigantic candy box of the most garish variety, the kind you sometimes win at a cheap carnival. The building is rapidly being taken over by the vines and other, less gentle vegetation, and there are only a few who remember when Pavlova danced there and the entire *corps de ballet* was imported from La Scala.

In those days Manáos was also the world's largest diamond market; now there are no more diamonds, and most of the rubber barons have died in poverty. The marble palaces they built have fallen into disrepair, and their children, who once played with toys made of gold, are either working in Manáos, some as civil servants, one as a streetcar conductor, or have returned to Europe.

Nevertheless, Manáos is not a ghost town, although the jungle eternally threatens to envelop it. The streets are wide and leisurely, and the trees and shrubs on either side are neatly trimmed; the huge cathedral is kept in perfect condition, fronted by a long walk which is lined with palm trees all of an identical height.

Most of the houses are of a glistening white with fluted red tile roofs, framed by well-kept public gardens in which there are always huge flowers in a dozen colors. It rains almost daily, seldom for more than a few minutes, usually in the early afternoon; thus vegetation flourishes.

There are good schools, handsome public buildings, little-theater groups, amateur symphonies, fine open-air cafés, shops with good although expensive merchandise, barbers who do their work in the open, wandering bakers who advertise their approach by blowing a bugle, and thousands of vultures who, in addition to what I was assured was an excellent sewage system, help keep the streets and boulevards free of debris.

Manáos has no railroad station, but a reasonably modern streetcar line encircles the city, making it almost impossible to believe that within a few steps on any side there are in the dense jungle scores of avaricious wild animals and boas.

The temperature seldom goes above ninety-five degrees and never falls below fifty-five; the average is a pleasant sixty-six to -eight. The Río Negro at this point is four miles wide, and has a high-water mark about sixty feet above the low-water mark. In late June of each year the temperature in the inky black waters drops so suddenly that hundreds of small fish often die, and the natives wear top coats and sleep under blankets for a few days. F. M. McDermott, an English explorer-scientist who investigated this phenomenon in the early 1930's explains that "the cause of this cold wind and water stream originates over the Pacific. The comparatively warm 'Chinook' wind strikes the highest Andes, melts the snows, and whistles through the bleak passes, which rob it of heat, and comes down with the snow-water through the Equatorial forest of the Amazon plains."

Fortunately I missed the brief cold spell, and my first afternoon in Manaós was pleasantly warm and leisurely. I had a pastry and three cups of thick black coffee at a sidewalk café, read the local newspapers, and watched the maids scrub the front steps of the houses, which are as white and shining as the best in Baltimore.

At that moment I agreed with that Brazilian, whoever he was, who called Manaós "that rare jewel lost in the wilderness." The days when a single canoe filled with rubber was worth $2500 are gone, but even if Manaós were not in the midst of the densest jungle in the world it would still be a memorable city. What's more, I think I've never met friendlier people anywhere. Nobody has much to do, and nobody any longer expects to become rich; so the people of Manaós spend their time being gracious—at least most of them do.

My experience at the hotel that night was somewhat less fortunate. I first had a lonely dinner, waiting for Catani to appear, but she did not. Then I had a few drinks in the bar, all of which were paid for by two slightly drunken traveling salesmen who had recently arrived from Bogotá and filled me in on the gossip back home. About midnight I went to bed.

There was only one sheet on the dilapidated mattress, but it was warm; so I took off my clothes and lay down nude on top, placing my head on a pillow which must have been at least a foot thick.

I don't know what the pillow was stuffed with, not feathers certainly; it did not give way at all under the weight of my head, and the rest of my body sank almost to the floor.

I got up to investigate and found that the spring mattress was so old that its elasticity was completely gone. Finally I unpacked my hammock, hung it between the window and the door, and immediately fell asleep.

The next afternoon a bellboy delivered a note scrawled in a cramped Spencerian hand and signed, "Respectfully, Da Silva." It asked, if I would be so kind, for me to come to his and Catani's suite at 3 P.M. It added, "I have a rare and important suggestion to make to you."

I arrived at the ornately furnished suite, which was usually reserved for visiting VIPs, exactly at 3:00, dressed in a freshly pressed white suit, my hair slicked back, my nails manicured, and feeling a little nervous. Señor da Silva, wearing an expensive but tasteful red silk dressing gown, was sitting up in bed, and Catani, in the green dress, was in a chair at his side, pretending to read a dog-eared South American picture magazine.

Da Silva's color had improved considerably and it was now that of slightly grimy parchment. He motioned me to sit down in a straight-backed chair on the other side of the bed.

"I had hoped," he began, "to talk to you about a business proposition this afternoon, but I now find my head is not as clear as I wish. Thus I will only make a simple request of you. I want you to show Manáos to Catani. I shall reimburse you for whatever expenses you incur."

I rose and shook my head. "I'm sorry, Señor da Silva," I said. "I shall be delighted to show Catani the town, but I must pay the expenses."

Da Silva's evil old face broke into a malicious grin. "My, you are young," he said. "I was never so youthful. I learned at a very early age to take whatever money was offered me for whatever purpose, no questions asked.

"However," he added, shrugging his gigantic shoulders, "I respect your wishes. Now go and have a good time."

Catani rose, and, as I shut the door after us, I looked back. Da Silva had half closed his eyes, but I knew that he was still watching us through the narrow slits remaining. I thought I heard him chuckle, but could not be sure.

Catani and I had a wonderful time. We walked through the public gardens; we drank coffee and ate pastries at sidewalk cafés; we tiptoed through the quiet, dark cathedral; we looked in awe at the huge opera house; we had a reasonably good steak and a lot of superb wine at one of Manáos' best cafés, and we ended the evening at a kind of night club where a superb guitarist accompanied a beautiful young boy who moaned plaintive Spanish songs, almost all of them having to do with the fact that love is short-lived.

When I said good night to Catani in the darkened lobby of the hotel, her cheeks were bright with color.

"In all my life," she said, "I have never had such a good time. I have never laughed so much."

"I'm glad," I said, squeezing her hand. "We'll do it again tomorrow."

Her face was suddenly serious. "No," she said, "no more. Señor da Silva and I are leaving soon for Rio, and this was the end for me.

"And," she added softly, "for you."

What a remarkable woman, I thought. Manáos was surely the largest city she had ever visited, in fact the only town of any size she had ever been in, but throughout the entire afternoon and evening she had acted as if she were accustomed to the most cosmopolitan life. Not once had she shown any surprise; she had what a very few women are born with and some acquire but others never achieve, true sophistication.

Da Silva was sitting in a darkened corner of the café Bar Americano when I arrived the following afternoon in response to a second note.

It was exactly two forty-five, and he was finishing a small cup of black coffee. He was wearing a white suit which, I felt certain, he had put on only a few minutes before.

"You are prompt, Señor Acebes," he said, motioning for me to sit down and glancing at the elaborately jeweled watch he carried in a pocket of his vest. "I appreciate promptness. I have studied the maxims of the ancients, accepting those that seem to me useful, rejecting others. Promptness is useful."

He ordered a glass of wine for me and another for himself. "As I told you," he went on, "I seldom have liquor in the daytime, but this is an exception. I had to talk to you."

When the waiter placed our drinks on the table, Da Silva took off his glasses and began polishing them with a huge white silk handkerchief. He did not replace them until after we had finished our conversation, probably because without them he looked rather helpless, which at the moment was the way he wanted to look.

"Señor Acebes," he said, leaning forward, his small, piglike eyes suddenly gleaming ominously. "I shall get to the point immediately. How would you like to make a small fortune?"

He picked up his glass of wine and began sipping it daintily, but his tiny eyes never left my face.

I smiled. "Everybody would like to make a small fortune," I said, "under the proper circumstances."

His eyes did not move; it was as if he had not heard me.

"When I was your age," he went on, "I explored many rivers of the Upper Amazon looking for rubber and balatá. In one of my explorations I came upon deposits of diamonds.

"These two," he said, indicating the large diamond tiepin and the even larger stone in the ring on his finger, "came from there.

"Unhappily, I had too many people with me at the time, and I did not wish them to know about my find. I got only these two out. I planned always to return, but I never did, and now I am too old.

"But," and he returned the half-empty wineglass to the table and leaned closer to me. I could see that his face was wet with sweat.

"But," he repeated, "you are young. I want you to organize and head an expedition into this area. I shall finance it, and we will go halves on what you find.

"I come to you because only an experienced man could enter the territory, a man who knows Indians and their psychology. These are not friendly Indians. Most of them have never seen a white man, but I am sure they can be handled.

"I found the two diamonds I am wearing at the bottom of a

crystalline creek. The large deposits are at the head of the creek, about a hundred miles upriver.

"You can find them." He sat back in his chair, returned the glasses to his nose, and smiled in what he probably thought was a benevolent manner.

"Now," he said, "you can see why on the boat I asked you so many questions about yourself. I had to know. Now I do. What do you say?"

I was astounded, not so much because of the proposal but because of the calculating way he had used Catani to get me interested.

I think I laughed.

"Look, Señor da Silva," I said slowly and emphatically, "an expedition of this sort would be extremely dangerous, not only because of the Indians, but because of the men I would have to take with me. If we did find a lot of diamonds, murder would be very probable. Only one or two would return from the expedition, and I am not at all sure I would be among them.

"For me, it is too much of a risk to go off looking for diamonds. Naturally, if I came across some, I would stake a claim. As a matter of fact, I know of at least two places where I think there are diamonds. One of them is perhaps the place you have in mind." (Since then, large deposits of diamonds have been found in the Cerro Roraima and La Gran Sabana in Venezuela. One is the spot I meant.)

"My answer, then," I said, "is no. I am sorry."

The expression on Da Silva's face did not change.

"Well," he said, "I fear I have lost a woman, then."

"I don't think so," I replied. "I'd say you have lost a diamond mine."

"First," he said, raising his half-filled glass and draining it, "one is without diamonds, after that, without the woman."

He stood up and shook my hand. "I thank you," he said. "It has been a pleasure." Then he waddled out of the bar.

The next morning I left Manáos, and I did not see Da Silva or Catani again there.

8

As the Catalina flying boat put down on the Río Negro, Roberto Londoño, who was standing on the bank of the river, grinned and waved at us.

"Hi," he shouted. "Is this the madman Acebes?"

I nodded.

"Fine," he shouted back. "I shall try to make your last days on earth as pleasant as possible."

As we reached the shore, Londoño, a handsome, dark, curly-haired young man of twenty with a wide, gape-toothed smile, extended his hand.

"Welcome," he said, first to me, then to Severo and Teolo. "Welcome to San Felipe de Río Negro—your first stop and probably your last on your voyage of discovery up the Orinoco."

Londoño, who was the air lines representative in San Felipe and who also negotiated for the rubber his company flew back to Bogotá, is the kind of man who, after five minutes, treats you as if you were his lifelong friend. He is cheerful, aggressive, hard-working, and an extrovert, and he is a perfect man for the job in a lonely outpost two hundred and fifty miles from the fountain-head of the Orinoco River.

During my stay in San Felipe I was grateful that he talked

incessantly. I was worried. I was beginning the most important expedition of my life.

For years I had been warned against it, but ever since I was fourteen, when I first read Baron Alexander von Humboldt's account of his trip up the Orinoco in 1800 and his discovery of the link between the water systems of the Orinoco and the Amazon, I had known that someday I would make the same voyage and that I would go on. I would attempt to reach the headwaters of the River of Seven Stars, and I would explore some of those thousands of square miles on either side of the river which have never been penetrated by white men.

Men have been searching for the headwaters of the Orinoco for more than four hundred years now. The Spanish conquistadors went upriver—no one knows exactly how far—to find the fabled El Dorado; they failed. Catholic missionaries got as far as Esmeralda but could not go on. A North American named Dr. Herbert Spencer Dickey claimed to have found the source in 1931, and twelve years later a Brazilian expedition came across what its members insisted was a different source.

No one knew who was right or if anybody was, and since 1943 nobody had tried to find out. I might fail, but I was determined to try.

On each of my previous expeditions I had questioned anyone with any information, no matter how meager, on what I might expect to find as I continued up the only one of the world's major rivers about which so little is known. Stories varied, but they all agreed that mine would be a dangerous expedition. I was invariably told that beyond a certain point—and no one knew just where—I would either be turned back by savages who hated white men or be killed and very probably eaten by members of cannibalistic tribes.

206

In the Vaupés, for example, I talked with a man who had been a prisoner of a group of Orinoco Indians. When he was a boy, he said, the Indians had attacked the settlement in which he lived, killing everyone except him and an old woman. The woman died of exposure, and he said he had spent six months with the Indians before he was able to escape by floating down the river on a tree trunk until he reached the Río Negro.

During that time, he told me, he had roved through the jungles with the Indians, sharing their wild fruit, the often uncooked meat of whatever animals they could kill, and a white clay from the banks of the river, which they baked until it turned red.

"I was young," the man said, "and I was small and thin, hardly a tasty bite. Otherwise they would have eaten me, and, if you go into the region, they will surely devour you, probably raw."

I shrugged. Most of us are unreliable when discussing our own courage and the dangers to which we have been exposed. I felt that the Indians of the Upper Orinoco could not be very different from those I'd met on other expeditions, and the less contact they had had with white men the more hospitable they were likely to be. Besides, I have always distrusted all stories about "cannibalistic" Indians; such tribes are always around another turn in the river, in that clump of jungle over there—wherever you happen not to be.

In any case, by January 1951 I was ready to start my trip. I was going to find the source of the Orinoco.

That was the reason I was in San Felipe de Río Negro, along with Severo Vargas and his son Teolo. I knew both of them could be depended on. On other expeditions I had several times heard Severo tell my porters that he would stand by me until his last drop of blood had been shed.

I needed that kind of loyalty plus the kind of courage which will not allow a man to turn back despite rumors of considerable danger. Besides, Severo has an instinctive feeling for dealing with other Indians. Teolo was naturally less experienced than his father, but he was learning fast.

During the six-hour flight from Bogotá, Livermann, the blond, deep-blue-eyed veteran of the Luftwaffe who was our pilot, several times buzzed bands of roving Indians, quickly scattering them.

He always chortled. Severo, who had never flown before, was pale, and he frequently kept his eyes closed, and during the buzzing turned his face from the window. He was not amused. Neither was I, but Teolo treated the entire experience in exactly the way any other eighteen-year-old boy would have. He loved flying.

He was also delighted with San Felipe. After all, although by now he had visited both Bogotá and Quito, San Felipe, in contrast to his own village, still represented civilization, and Teolo was going to make the most of it. He had discovered that girls, including white ones, considered him attractive, and he had bought a pocket comb in Bogotá. Since then he had spent every spare moment combing his hair.

As he looked around San Felipe he took out the comb and went to work.

San Felipe consists of one well-built house, which was Londoño's headquarters. However, it was once a Spanish outpost during the lengthy and costly wars against the Portuguese of Brazil. The bell of the fort could, it is said, be heard for hundreds of miles in every direction. When the Spaniards left, apparently in something of a hurry, they buried the bell in the river. The fort itself is now barely discernible, the walls being visible only because the Río Negro has, during its periodic floods, deposited fresh earth around the remains. Four native huts are built on top of the old site.

Although, in the centuries since the Spanish abandoned their adventure in San Felipe, no one in the area has had the energy to find out, they all believe that a great treasure is buried beneath the bell. Some say it is diamonds; others are equally sure it is gold. A few are willing to settle for silver.

During my stay in San Felipe the children began referring to me as "the man who came out of the ground." They had heard that I was Spanish and were convinced that, after living under the fort for several hundred years, I had finally emerged to claim the treasure.

The Río Negro, which is about five hundred yards wide at this point, serves as the border between Colombia and Venezuela, and just across the way is the village of San Carlos. Communication between the two is easy; dugouts cross the river constantly.

San Carlos was founded more than three hundred years ago, and by 1820 it was already a flourishing center for boatbuilding. By 1910, during the height of the rubber boom, it had nearly two thousand inhabitants.

Now only a few more than three hundred remain. Most of the others fled in terror to Brazil in the years from 1913 to 1921, when a dictator who, on a smaller scale, was as ruthless and bloodthirsty as either Stalin or Hitler took over the territory of the Amazonas.

Tomás Funes was a businessman, and until the evening of May 8, 1913, he was considered a gentle, inoffensive little man with a good head for figuring profit and loss. His revolution, which, according to most accounts, lasted only about twenty minutes, began at San Fernando de Atabapo, which was then and still is headquarters for the region.

As happened later in Italy and in Germany, Funes' coup d'état was sponsored by solid businessmen who apparently believed that a man like Funes would bring law and order to the Amazonas Province of Venezuela. Besides, he had promised lower taxes.

However, immediately after he and his followers had killed the governor, taken his wife and two children as prisoners, and shot the handful of soldiers who were foolish enough to resist, Funes turned on his sponsors. He killed sixty-five that same evening, many with his own pistol.

"Tomás Funes was," an old Indian told me in San Carlos, "an excellent shot."

Funes was a businessman; he killed other businessmen because, as soon as he became a dictator, he determined to wipe out all competition, both financial and political. Before dawn of that bloody May night he also killed the only doctor in the whole region because the doctor had refused to poison one of Funes' enemies. For twenty-four years after that there was no doctor in all of Amazonas.

A few days after the revolution Funes ordered one of his lieutenants, a man called "El Avispa," to shoot a woman who refused to tell where her husband had fled. When "The Wasp" protested, Funes fingered his pistol, and "El Avispa" complied, first, however, allowing his troops to ravish the woman and murder her two small children.

Then Funes got down to serious murder. He ruled until January 1921, when he was overthrown and taken prisoner by an idealistic revolutionary named General Arevalo Cedeño.

On January 30, 1921, Funes and a henchman were executed, charged with the murder of 420 persons. Those were only the murders that were recorded, of course; there were others which were carried out in secret, and no one counted the number of

Indians who had been put to death by him. There may have been several thousand, some shot, others decapitated by machete, many simply placed in boats without paddles which invariably sank at a spot where thousands of sharp-toothed piranhas were waiting.

Other Indians who happened to be a little short in their quota of rubber were placed in stocks, were tied in ant heaps, or whipped to death.

Naturally Indian women were raped by the hundreds. Funes himself neither smoked nor drank, but he sometimes had as many as a dozen women in a single night—at least that is the legend in San Carlos. "Except for the women," the old Indian told me, "Funes was a moral man."

At the time of his execution there were those who regretted it. There still are.

"He was efficient," a resident of San Carlos who had better be nameless told me. "The Amazonas was booming when he was governor. We need another man like him to bring this area back to normal, a kinder man, of course, one somewhat less blood-thirsty."

San Carlos may never recover from the Funes rule, and as for the rubber trade, it is, of course, gone forever.

Meantime the village continues its lazy, uneventful existence.

Don Manuel Azavache, the prefect of San Carlos, is small in stature, no more than five two or three, I imagine, with the face of a world-weary saint, and a real gentleness of manner. On meeting him I immediately felt I had made a lifelong friend, which is one of the reasons so many accusations were to be thrown at me later.

Don Manuel, like almost everybody else in villages like San Carlos, was deeply religious. He attended mass on Sundays, dressed in his Sunday best. He nodded affirmatively when the priest denounced sin, particularly adultery. At the same time he was, like almost everyone else, living with an Indian woman many years younger than he, and was surrounded by children, the result of his somewhat casual union with a series of other women. "A man," said Don Manuel, "gets tired of having the same woman around *all* of the time.

"The human animal, especially the male of the species, needs variety." Don Manuel was a great detective story fan, and he had even tried to write some of his own, without much success. In addition he was a great conversationalist.

As a youth he had, he said, tried to reach the headwaters of the Orinoco himself, but the Venezuelan Government had refused him financial support. Nevertheless, he had ascended the Siapa River, accompanied by twelve men.

"The expedition was," he told me, "uneventful until one morning. It was a little after dawn, and we were about to have our morning coffee, when, without warning, out of the jungle appeared twenty-five warriors, each carrying a huge bow taut with an arrow. They were completely naked, and behind them were an equal number of women, also naked and carrying half a dozen arrows each, ready to pass them on to the men.

"They gazed at us in silence, and we gazed back. None of us moved; I was trembling so that I couldn't have if I'd wanted to.

"After what seemed to be an hour or more, but was probably only a few minutes, they apparently realized that we were not belligerent, and one of them, the largest, most muscular, and obviously the chief, motioned for the rest to hand their arrows to the women, which they did.

"Then they led us into the jungle and indicated a barely visible path; late that night we reached a cluster of shelters, which was their village, and they put us in one, an open-faced affair with a slanting roof made of leaves and a few thin palm branches.

"First, they quickly made a rude rack and indicated that they wanted us to put our guns on it, which we did. Although they had never seen guns before, they seemed to fear them.

"After that the women brought us a pulpy mixture of a disagreeable brownish color. It tasted worse than it looked, but I told the men to eat it all, and we did. I could scarcely keep it down, but I knew that this was a test and that failure to pass it would probably have meant death.

"After that we were given huge quantities of bananas, cooked meat, and a lot of food I couldn't identify but most of which was highly edible.

"Two Indians guarded us day and night, and we were allowed to leave the lean-to in pairs to relieve ourselves. By the eighth day my men had decided that there was no hope of escape, that we would die there.

"I somehow summoned up a courage I didn't know I had and told the men to get ready to leave. As soon as we began to pick up our guns and equipment, both guards ran screaming to the chief, but we did not stop.

"Instead, walking Indian fashion, in single file, we started to cross the village toward the jungle path. Men, women, and children ran out of their shelters and began shouting at us in a language we, of course, could not understand. Only the chief said nothing. He stood in the shadow of his doorway and watched us, looking, I thought, rather sad.

"No one attempted to stop us, and we went on, spending the first night on the open ground by the path. During the first day and the second half a dozen Indians caught up with us in the early morning, midafternoon, and evening, both days at exactly the same hours, and handed us food, which we accepted with nods of gratitude.

"On the morning of the third day we reached the banks of the river at the spot at which we had left the dugouts.

"Unfortunately the Indians did not appear that morning, although we waited until almost noon. I say it was unfortunate because I had planned to kidnap one and bring him back to San Carlos with us. I had rationalized myself into believing that one of the warriors would have been of scientific interest.

"On the way back we had one near accident. One of my men took a small dugout and went up a small stream to search for cabezón turtles. When, after several hours, he did not return, we went to look for him. A huge alligator was circling what looked like a deserted dugout, but, as we approached, the alligator submerged, and we found the man inside the dugout, seriously hurt but still alive. He had been surprised by the alligator while swimming after a turtle and in battle with the monster had been able, as so seldom happens, to stick his fingers in the alligator's eyes, then had worked his way back to the dugout, and with a final show of strength had thrown himself into it.

"He survived, but for the rest of his life his body was a mass of scars.

"That was my first and last brush with adventure. Since then I have been living quietly in San Carlos, reading the few detective stories I can lay hands on, changing my bed companions when the mood demands it, and watching life pass me by, knowing I shall not achieve posterity by finding the headwaters of this strange and dark river. That is your challenge."

Don Manuel was the only one in San Carlos or, for that matter, anywhere else who encouraged me.

"Ah," he would say, "if only I were thirty years younger, I would go with you, at whatever cost."

The first thing I discovered in San Felipe was that I needed an outboard motor. No one was willing to become a paddler, no matter what the pay. The population of both San Felipe and of San Carlos, as is true in most villages along the Orinoco, is made up mainly of *caboclos* and *zambos*, people who call themselves white but who actually are a kind of ethnological mystery. They usually have a good deal of Indian blood, some Spanish, some Negro, and occasionally even a little Chinese.

They are inordinately proud, often vain, usually lazy, and frequently dishonest. It took a long time to find six men who would consent to work for me at all, let alone paddle a dugout up the Orinoco, a job they considered suitable only for their inferiors, pure-blooded Indians.

I had decided I needed half a dozen helpers on the expedition, in addition to Teolo and Severo. Although I did not mention it at the time, that number would be necessary in case the motor broke down; in that case paddling would be necessary, but by then it would be too late to turn back.

In addition I assumed that the river would be impossible to navigate at various points, and I would have to leave the boat and part of the equipment with at least four men to guard against theft. I would then continue with the rest and as many savage Indian porters as I could hire until I reached my destination.

Finally, after a good deal of persuasion, I got one man to sign, mainly, I believe, because his clothes were nearly worn out, and four others immediately followed. The first was Simón García, an amiable Negro with the thin, tight-lipped features of an aristocrat; I suspected then and found out for sure later that he was the strongest-willed of the lot, except for Severo and Teolo. The others were Venancio López, Francisco Brice, Manuel Padrón (Chinchena), and Pablo Guimará.

Unfortunately the day before I embarked a group of Curripaco Indians arrived in San Felipe. I would much rather have had them accompany me. They had not been softened by contact with civilization, at least of the San Felipe-San Carlos variety.

However, it was too late. My crew had already been paid two months' salary in advance, as was the custom. Most of it was merchandise from the general store and some which I had brought from Bogotá. They took machetes, belts, ammunition, a little food, and trousers and shirts of khaki. To discover whether the trousers fitted, they picked them up by the waist, holding the front with one hand, the back with the other; then they lifted them to their necks, and if their hands met in the backs of their necks, they considered the waist a perfect fit. To measure the length of the legs, they took the trousers by the cuff ends and stretched them at arm's length across their chests.

The method was not exactly scientific, according to, say, Brooks Brothers standards, but it seemed to work well enough. Besides, they used clothes only to cover their nakedness; their vanity they displayed by the elaborateness of the belts they chose.

Meantime a five-horsepower motor was flown in from Bogotá as well as forty-five gallons of gasoline. In addition Don Manuel telegraphed his son Miguel in Puerto Ayacucho, and a few days later Miguel arrived in a good-sized launch, bringing three additional drums of gasoline with fifty gallons in each plus fifteen gallons of oil.

Altogether I spent eighteen days in San Felipe. During that time I used every spare moment—and most of them were spare—to find out all I could about the Upper Orinoco.

The area into which I was headed is inhabited by three groups of Indians, the Maquiritares, the Guaharibos, and the Guaicas.

The Maquiritares, who inhabit the region from La Esmeralda

down the Orinoco and up the Cunucunuma River have had much contact with the whites. From La Esmeralda to the Ocamo tributary are the Guaharibos, savages who steal from the white man but let him go unharmed.

From the Ocamo tributary on are the Guaicas. Nobody I talked to had seen them or even knew anyone who had, but it was rumored that the Guaicas killed any stranger, white or Indian, on sight. Five years earlier, I was told, they had waged a long war of extermination against each other, finally being driven back by the Maquiritares and the Guaharibos, who united against them and forced them to retreat to the Upper Orinoco and the Upper Siapa.

Beyond that no one had any information.

My plan was to pick up two Maquiritares and take them with me into the territory of the Guaharibos, then to use the same procedure, hiring two Guaharibos and going into Guaica country. From then on I would be in completely unknown territory, assuming, of course, I got that far. Almost no one in San Carlos or San Felipe thought I would.

Amazonas, a husky, dark-skinned Brazilian of about thirty who was waiting in San Carlos for a boat to take him to Manáos, told me that numerous small parties going into the land of the Guaharibos in search of timber had been driven out, completely nude, with handkerchiefs tied around their heads.

"The Guaharibos seem to want hats more than any other article of clothing," he said. "I once had my hat taken by an elderly Guaharibo who wore nothing else. I was frightened, but his appearance was so ludicrous that I couldn't help laughing. He laughed with me, but he didn't return my hat.

"However, except for catching a bad cold, I suffered no ill effects from my capture. I had been on a short expedition with an

American missionary and his wife and a very fat businessman from a place called Omaha, Nebraska.

"We had decided to cook our dinner on a beach upstream, then the Guaharibos surrounded us; they disrobed us right there, six to ten of them working on each of us. They were neither excited nor hurried. They simply took off our clothes, being careful not to harm us, and while they worked they chatted and laughed with each other, particularly as they undressed the fat man. He was shaking so much that it looked as if his belly had an electric vibrator attached. On the other hand, the missionary and his wife accepted the whole situation calmly.

"They were fine people and, naked as the day they were born, had just as much dignity as if they had been fully clothed.

"When the Indians had finished taking off our clothes, they released us. By the time we got back to the nearest settlement, our bodies were blue with cold. It was nearly midnight, but as soon as we'd borrowed some clothes and had some hot coffee, we all laughed—all except the fat man from Omaha, Nebraska.

"He said he was going to speak to the American consul about the inadequate police protection in the Orinoco area."

Amazonas chortled at the memory.

"As a matter of fact," he said, "the only time I ever heard of anybody being hurt by the Guaharibos was when they captured a Negro. Apparently they'd never seen a black man before, because they rubbed his skin with sand until he bled all over; they seemed to feel he was white underneath.

"When they found out they were wrong, they let him go."

On the other hand, a man in San Carlos whose name I've forgotten told me that a few years back a party of twenty had had a less happy experience. After reaching a Guaharibo village and making friends with the Indians they started to cook their dinner.

At one point a Guaharibo who had been watching wide-eyed with the others ran up and grabbed a piece of wild pig which was roasting in the fire.

One of the white men reached over and slapped him across the face.

The Indian did not cry out, and there was not a sound from the others, but in a few minutes the entire village was abandoned by the Guaharibos. The next morning, my informant said, the twenty men were ambushed in the jungle and eighteen of them murdered.

"Only two escaped," he concluded, "and they never returned to the Orinoco."

Severo, who had heard the story, grunted, then laughed heartily. I could tell he was impressed, but I did not know in what way.

The next morning he told me. "These men had only themselves to blame," he said. "When you strike an Indian you must expect him to strike back. The Indian, too, is a man."

On day when Londoño and I were taking an early afternoon siesta, we were awakened by a slight crash outside the window. It was during the carnival season, an occasion which is celebrated with great lavishness in cities like Rio de Janeiro, with parades and elaborate costumes and masks and great parties. In places like San Carlos the feeling of festivity is just as strong, but there is only one thing to do, get drunk, or, if you are a young girl, try to throw someone in the river, which is considered a highly entertaining sport.

When Londoño and I crept to the window, we saw eight young girls outside, holding in their laughter. One of them had fallen over a wooden pail in the doorway which had made the noise. We immediately barricaded the doors, but the girls refused to leave, and they kept shouting invitations for us to come out, questioning our manhood if we refused to do so. Finally, after about an hour, we both put on pants and short-sleeved shirts and stepped outside.

The girls immediately grabbed us, four each, propelled us to the river, and threw us in, laughing and shouting. The afternoon was considered a great success.

Except for Londoño and myself there was at the time only one other Colombian in either San Carlos or San Felipe. He was called Belleza (Beauty), and he was the ugliest man I've ever seen. He was short, about my height; he had small, close-set eyes, an underslung jaw, and a crooked, completely untrustworthy but strangely attractive smile. He looked like an unsuccessful race-track tout or a tenth-rate gangster.

"You be careful of Belleza, Señor Acebes," Don Manuel told me. "He will carve out your heart with a smile on his face, and you will drop dead before you know he has even touched you."

I paid no attention to the warning. Belleza fascinated me. Although he was only thirty-two, he had had enough adventures for a dozen lifetimes, even if only half of what he told me is true. I am reasonably certain that all of it is. He is the kind of man who would not lie unless there were something to be gained by it.

When he was only nine years old, he said, a screaming mob of bandits attacked the settlement of Támara in which he lived. He had been given a revolver to help defend the village, but in his excitement he shot the nose off an old woman who was leaning out of a window.

"She never forgave me, Señor Acebes," he said, "and I cannot understand, for what happened was only an accident.

"Besides, she was a very ugly woman, and she looked most unbeautiful, with or without her nose."

In his early twenties he had set out to see the world and, of course, to make his fortune.

"It was very dull there," he said, "and also I had risen as far as I could in such a place. I had started as a messenger boy and at nineteen was already the telegraph operator. Of interesting messages there were none; so I left."

He then joined a group of llaneros who were driving a herd of cattle to Villavicencio. However, he became separated from the rest, and one evening when he was on the Meta River going in the direction of Orocue, his dugout turned over, and he lost all of his belongings and clothes. He had been sleeping when the boat overturned, and he waded ashore in his underwear.

"Besides," he said, "they were not very good underwears. In them were many holes."

He wandered aimlessly for an hour or so, shivering with the cold, until he came across a Plana Indian chief.

"I begged of him to take me with him. I said I would live as one of his tribe," Belleza went on. "I had lost all, and it made no difference to me where I went."

The chief agreed, but he named one condition. He told Belleza that if he lived with the tribe, he must never leave it, and, if he tried, he would be put to death. Mr. Beauty agreed.

"From then on it was as if I was an Indian. I threw away the underwear and put on a loincloth; I even carried bows and arrows. I hunted when the others hunted; I fought when they fought, and when I felt the need for a woman all were available to me. My skin was burned dark by the sun, but I was still lighter in color than their men, and I was much admired.

"It is true that I slept in the palm groves like an animal, but I had with me a different squaw each night.

"As time went on, however, I became most restless. I helped

221

in the stealing of cattle, and once I made an expedition into one of the white settlements for the taking of arms and merchandise for the tribe. It was not, however, of a success.

"I was told that there was not far distant an iron house built by the Spaniards in which there was much gold. The Indians knew this because when they shot arrows in the windows, they put a gluey substance on them, and, when they withdrew the arrows, gold coins were stuck to the glue.

"They did not go into the house because a great gold snake inside guarded the treasure, they believed.

"However," he sighed, "they would never tell me the place of the iron house. I do not believe, Señor Acebes, that they trusted me. I do not know why.

"I looked for the house myself, but could not find it."

Eventually Belleza got hungry for salt, which almost none of the Indians have. They do not seem to need it.

"It is so small a thing, salt," said Belleza, "but I hungered for it, as for a woman, and I knew I must leave."

He escaped late at night and for three days thereafter, wearing only his loincloth and carrying a bow and a few arrows, he wandered over the llanos.

On the third night he came to the lonely house of a Venezuelan, who gave him trousers and a shirt, and then Belleza went down the Yucao River until he came to the Meta. After that he went to a small village with about fifty inhabitants, Cabuyero, where he became secretary to the mayor.

"This mayor," he said, "was a most dull man. To him nothing ever happened; besides, the village was so small that there was almost no opportunity for the taking of bribes.

"Again I was much bored, and I went to Villavicencio and got a job with the Shell Oil."

Shell sent him to the newly founded settlement of Puerto López. "There," he said, "I also became a butcher. There was not enough of meat, and of money there was plenty. So I sold meat."

In addition, in the evenings he played the guitar and sang at the village dances. "Many gringos came to Puerto López," he said, "and I would tell them my story, and then of me they would take many photographs as of a strange animal.

"I asked them to pay for the taking of the pictures, and they did, complaining only a little."

Finally he also wangled the job of secretary of Puerto López, a position in which, I imagine, some graft was available. Mr. Beauty would not confirm my suspicions. He simply grinned knowingly when I asked.

However, he saved a good deal of money from his several sources of income, and after a time he again returned to Villavicencio.

"It was this same boredom in Puerto López," he said. "I am a man easily bored. Besides, there were few women there. The dullness you cannot believe if I told you even."

There were many women in Villavicencio, and there was liquor, and in a few weeks Belleza was penniless again.

At that point he joined an itinerant gambler who was also a medicine man. "We sold herbs of many mixtures," said Mr. Beauty, "and all of the mixtures were said to cure everything. It was very profitable because, you see, the herbs were without cost to us. We picked them up on the way from town to town and placed them in bottles. That is the reason the mixtures were so many."

He and his partner would set up their business in the public square; then the gambler would sell the herbs after first making his sales pitch. In the evening the gambling table would be opened, and Belleza would wander up and place several bets. He always won, and as he walked away with his pockets filled with pesos the villagers would fall all over each other in their eagerness to place bets.

"It is," Belleza sighed philosophically, "impossible to keep people from making fools of themselves if they wish."

A little later, after he and the gambler parted company, Mr. Beauty went back to Villavicencio once more. "And this time I found myself associated with a counterfeiter of gold. I did not myself do any of this counterfeiting. I only *watched* how it was done. It was most interesting.

"However, as I would walk down the streets of Villavicencio, the police would look most suspiciously at me. So I retired, and I went to Puerto Ayacucho, a place I had never been before."

There he again played his guitar for anyone who would pay to listen, and he also became a bullfighter.

The bullfights in these areas are not quite the same as those in the cities of Mexico and Spain. An elderly bull is brought into the village square, and on carnival days a man like Mr. Beauty teases him for a while, usually finding that his hardest job is to keep the bull from going to sleep.

However, bullfighting is popular, and, as Belleza said, "It takes not much skill, and the bullfighter is much admired by many, especially women. I always have many women when I fight the bull, several on the same night.

"It is sometimes most tiring."

From Puerto Ayacucho, Belleza had come to San Felipe, where he called himself a rubber trader. I never saw him do any trading, but he always seemed to have enough money for food and drink.

He never paid for the women he had. "For Belleza to pay money for women," he said, "would be a blot on his honor. I am considered a great lover, why I do not know, perhaps because of my great beauty."

And he laughed.

One night at a dance in San Carlos he became very drunk, and when he got to the river to cross to San Felipe he got in the wrong dugout. As he started paddling across, he got water in the dugout, and a duck in the back began protesting loudly.

Belleza was so surprised that he struck the duck on the head, killing it instantly.

At the same time the dugout turned over, and Belleza found himself in the middle of the Río Negro. He sobered up instantly, grabbed the duck, righted the dugout, and paddled back to San Carlos, where the angry owner of the dugout and the duck was waiting for him.

As he stepped out of the boat, dripping water, Belleza began weeping, and as he handed the dead duck to its owner he said, "It is most sad, sir. The duck is drowned, and I myself was nearly drowned in trying to rescue it."

The owner's anger vanished immediately, and he invited Mr. Beauty to have dinner at his house the next evening.

"The roasted duck is most delicious," Belleza told me. "There was also much of drinking and some of gambling.

"I won much of money."

By February 15 we were ready to leave San Carlos—or thought we were.

I had bought two craft, one a two-ton boat mounted on a dugout for a base, the other a small dugout which I hoped would be easy to maneuver in case we had to abandon the larger boat on the Upper Orinoco.

I had sent the small dugout five days ahead attached to a mail launch. It would be waiting for us at Capihuara on the Casiquiare channel near its entrance into the Orinoco.

I knew that the larger craft already had a heavy load for a five-horsepower motor, but we went ahead anyway. We had not gone more than five hundred yards, which took almost an hour, when I realized what a more experienced explorer would probably have known already. Our load was so badly distributed that it was impossible to go on.

So we returned to San Carlos, and that afternoon I had the men reload the boat and remove the carroza, or palm roof, which was not only heavy but unsteady. The sun beating down on our heads all day would be uncomfortable, but comfort would have to be sacrificed for speed and safety.

Just as we were about ready to start a second time, Cabo Perales, commander of La Guardia Nacional of San Carlos, offered to tow our boat past the first rapid of the Casiquiare, where, he said, we were almost certain to have trouble. I agreed since his patrol boat had a twenty-two-horsepower motor.

The following morning we got under way once more a little after dawn.

This time we got two hundred yards up the Río Negro when the motor on the patrol boat fell into the river. The cord by which it should have been made fast in the boat was instead being held by Perales and when the motor started slipping he let go of the cord.

When I was able to speak, I quietly asked him why.

"The motor was pulling me into the river," he said, wiping huge drops of perspiration from his forehead, "and I cannot swim."

I said several unpleasant English words under my breath, and then we once more went back to San Carlos. The motor had fallen at a spot where the water was only about four yards deep, but because of the current it took twenty men a day and a half to rescue it.

Naturally a dance was held in San Carlos that night to celebrate. I watched for a while, and then Perales came over with a barefoot twelve-year-old, one of those Londoño liked to refer to as "the high-society girls of San Carlos."

Perales insisted that I dance with her, and I did, although it was impossible to keep in step with the erratic rhythm of the orchestra—a guitar and a pair of maracas. I was afraid of stepping on the girl's bare toes with my heavy boots, and the top of her head came only up to my then heavily bearded chin.

I never was sure exactly what she looked like. The room was dimly lighted, and every time I would try to get a glimpse of her face, she would lower her head and giggle like any other twelve-year-old.

However, she was fully developed physically and no doubt had already had several affairs with the older men. Adultery is common among both sexes, as I've said, and the illegitimate children resulting from unblessed sexual unions are not looked down upon. They are cared for with the rest.

Sex is uncomplicated—although often a little startling. I was told that when a thirty-year-old man in San Carlos asked a four-year-old girl to go to bed with him, she simply said, "Oh yes, if you only knew where I hang my hammock."

Just before I arrived a nine-year-old girl had finally been cured of gonorrhea, given her by a census taker visiting San Carlos.

However, in the afternoons I saw her playing with the other children, apparently not affected by her experience.

As Londoño put it, "Virginity in newly born girls is something of an anomaly."

Londoño and I left the dance early that night, and as we stepped off the dugout in San Felipe we saw Severo standing in the shadows of the headquarters. He was swaying slightly.

"How are you, Señor Hector?" he shouted, grinning foolishly.

I smiled. "You look sort of tipsy, Severo," I said.

He roared with laughter. "I am, Señor Hector; I am much drunk. I, too, had to celebrate the taking out of the motor."

He laughed again, but for a moment seemed almost sober. "Besides," he went on, "the people here say we won't come back. They say the Guaicas are going to kill us."

He hiccuped. "I must celebrate while I can," he said.

Then he stepped closer to me and in a loud stage whisper said, "I must apologize, Señor Hector. I have drunk two bottles of the rum you gave me to put away."

I had put five bottles of rum in Severo's care, to be used in case of snakebite or after a heavy rain or as a stimulant following a particularly wearing day.

I shrugged. "All right, Severo," I said. "You get yourself a good night's sleep now. We're starting early in the morning."

"I need more to drink," he said. "Another bottle of rum, perhaps?"

I shook my head, and Severo sadly turned and walked back toward the hut where he slept. However, I had a feeling that his celebration was not yet finished, and I later discovered that all five bottles of the rum had disappeared.

Just before sunrise the next morning Severo appeared in the doorway of Londoño's headquarters, where I was having breakfast. His eyes were slightly bloodshot, and his hands trembled a little, but otherwise he seemed to have recovered.

He kept his eyes lowered as he spoke. "I have something to tell you, Señor Hector," he said.

"Come in, Severo," I said. "You needn't apologize for drinking the rum. Such things happen."

He still did not look up, and he kept his huge hands behind his back, as if he were ashamed of them.

"It is not that," he went on, "although I am sorry. What I am to say now will displease you more."

I waited, not replying.

After a long pause he continued. "I have decided, Señor Hector, that I wish to return to Ecuador."

I was so stunned I was unable to reply.

Naturally I had expected trouble on this expedition, and I was by no means satisfied with the men I had hired at San Carlos. I considered them useless but necessary.

But I had felt I could be sure of Severo and Teolo. Now Severo was trying to back out. If he did, I would have to turn back.

I looked at him, and for just a moment his eye caught mine. I could see that he was ashamed.

"Look," I said. "Go find Teolo, and after I've finished eating I want to see both of you in my room."

He nodded, and without a word opened the door and went outside.

A few minutes later he and Teolo appeared in my room. I invited them to sit on the bed, and then I began talking. I think I have never been more eloquent. There was never more need for it.

"Listen carefully, Severo," I said. "When I thought of you as the man to accompany me on this expedition, I had a very good reason for it. I knew you could be trusted. I was sure you wouldn't fail me just because some risk might be involved.

"I am not asking you to go ahead of me, but only to follow. You know I am not going to risk my own life and those of the rest of you unnecessarily.

"Nor am I going to become panicky just because of some wild rumors about Indians no outsider knows anything about. Let's find out for ourselves. I promise you that at the first sign of real danger we will all come back."

I paused, looking first at Teolo, who, since he was young, did not know the meaning of fear, then at Severo, who had never acknowledged it before.

"Are you with me?" I asked.

Teolo spoke first, not waiting for his father's approval.

"When do we leave, Señor Hector?" he asked, grinning eagerly.

For just a moment there was silence. Then Severo spoke.

"I am with you," he said.

He turned and left the room, followed by Teolo.

A few minutes later I went into Londoño's office and typed out six copies of the following document:

San Carlos de Río Negro
Venezuela
February 18, 1951.

I ———————————, resident of the area of San Carlos de Río Negro, Venezuela, declare in this document, and before witnesses, that I am accompanying Señor Hector R. Acebes in an expedition to the Upper Orinoco of my own free will and at all risks.

In request for not knowing
how to sign

FOR ——————
Y ——————

Witnesses:

It took some persuasion to convince the members of the crew that they should sign, and I realized that if they really wanted to

230

desert me their "x's" on a piece of paper would be meaningless. However, I thought the document might have some psychological value.

Simón, the thin-faced Negro who, since he had said he knew the area into which we were going, I had made the leader, along with Severo, was the first to put his mark on the document. The others docilely followed his example.

By that time it was nine-thirty, two hours later than our scheduled starting time, but I realized that another day's delay might mean the end of the expedition.

So we climbed into the boat and started up the Río Negro. Roberto Londoño was standing on the San Felipe side, and across the way in San Carlos it looked as if almost the entire population was lined up to see us off.

Nevertheless, there was no shouting. There was instead a kind of ominous silence, and, when I looked back, Londoño, who had been waving and smiling, looked sad and apprehensive.

When he saw me watching him, he lifted his hand and grinned again.

"Bon voyage," he shouted. "Bon voyage."

"See you soon," I shouted back, but my words were lost in the wind that swept across the river.

9

A little after sundown that afternoon we arrived at Solano, one of the two villages still left on the Casiquiare channel, which is surely the most unusual body of water anywhere in the world.

The Casiquiare flows out of the Orinoco, takes a southwestern course and then joins the Río Negro, which in turn flows into the Amazon. Thus South America's two great rivers are united.

In its east to southwest course the Casiquiare is about two hundred and fifty miles long, about one hundred and fifty yards wide in most places, and an average of less than four yards in depth. At its lower extreme the water is a magnificent inky black in color, but the upper part abruptly becomes an ugly yellow-brown. The banks lining the muddy part of the channel are infested with millions of flies; the shores on either side of the black waters have no flies at all. No one knows why.

The residents of Solano insist that during the winter months the channel flows from the Orinoco to the Río Negro, and during the summer in the opposite direction, but the water always flows from the Orinoco to the Río Negro.

There is considerable evidence that the channel is navigable for canoes all the year round, although most people in San Carlos and San Felipe insist that it is not. I found the current was wonderfully mild, even after Capihuara, where I was told I might find it impossible to navigate the larger of my two boats.

What's more, an hour or so after San Carlos and San Felipe were out of sight, I began to feel that well being I find only on an expedition. In the distance were smooth, sandstone cliffs spotted with bright green vegetation in the most modern designs; further off were clumps of jungle against the blue-gray of the horizon, and once, far away, I saw the silver of a tiny lake.

A capybara emerged from the jungle, walked to the bank of the river, regarded me solemnly for a moment, then plunged into the water. A tapir swam undisturbed beside us for a while. A sloth blinked curiously from a tree, then went back to sleep, still in its ridiculous upside-down position.

I watched for a while and listened to the eternal song and chatter of a million birds; I looked up at the sun, which was beginning what would be the kind of sunset unknown outside the jungle. I closed my eyes for a moment.

When I awakened we were in Solano.

Solano is a tiny village with only sixty-five inhabitants, but most of them had been away, working in the jungle for several months, and only a handful remained.

Vegetation choked the village square, grew high on the narrow, muddy main street, and threatened to envelop the cluster of deserted huts. The look of desolation and despair was everywhere.

Nelo Maldonado, our host that night, was an enormous elderly Negro who had come from Trinidad in an unsuccessful search for gold and then had settled in Solano, "To wait," as he said, "for death to overtake me." There are many Negroes in the area, most of them descendants of slaves who escaped from Brazil into Venezuela, where they were free.

Maldonado himself was said by his neighbors to be a fearsome man; he was rumored to have been a pirate in his youth, which was quite a long time ago, although he was not a hundred years old, as I was told, only about seventy. He was alleged to have been a bandit, a political conspirator, and a murderer. Now he was prefect of this quiet village.

"Why," one of his constituents said, "he has three hundred murders on his soul."

Maldonado himself was a quiet man, but when I, laughing, of course, asked him about the rumors, he frowned.

"Why," he said, "I have never killed one man even, except in self-defense. Naturally in a long life I have seen some men die— accidentally.

"But it is not three hundred. It is not one hundred, even."

One of Maldonado's wives or mistresses or servants gave us a magnificent dinner of roast wild pig, and we all retired almost

233

immediately after eating. The next morning I was on my way again at dawn.

We spent the second night on the bank of the Caño de Santa Cruz, a narrow river which flows into the Casiquiare. It is no more than eighteen to twenty feet wide and is completely roofed by a thick tangle of green-brown vegetation.

We made camp near the temporary home of a short, powerfully built man named Rondón, who, with his Indian wife, a baby less than six months old, and two teen-aged daughters lived in a shelter which consisted of four sticks haphazardly driven into the ground and covered with a roof of palm leaves just large enough to keep off the rain—if they huddled close together.

Like so many others in the area, they had only enough clothes to cover their nakedness, and their food, including that of the baby, consisted of meat from the animals killed by Rondón. The rest he salted for sale later in San Carlos. Hunting is not very profitable in such areas.

However, the Rondóns seemed to be healthy enough, and that night the baby yelled normally for several hours.

Our third night we spent at the house of Pablo Guimará, one of the men I had hired in San Felipe. I did my best to persuade his sister-in-law, a light-skinned girl with a voluptuous figure and a pleasant, toothy smile, to come along with us as cook, but she refused. The Guaharibos would certainly steal her, she said, and besides, she was planning an early marriage. To date, she admitted, no candidate had appeared, but she was hopeful, and I noticed her appraising the width of Teolo's broad shoulders.

He disappeared shortly after dark and didn't show up again until the next morning, looking rather wan but with his hair neatly combed, as usual.

Just before we left, a group of men from the settlement—

which consisted of three tumble-down shacks—returned with twenty cabezón turtles they had caught during the night. The cabezón is usually about ten to fifteen inches long and looks very much like any other turtle except for its beak, with resembles that of a parrot. A single snap of the beak can sever a finger, and I have heard of men dying from a stomach wound inflicted by a cabezón.

The people of the Casiquiare swim after the turtles and turn them over, then tow them to shore. Their meat is tender enough but is oily and tasteless without a great deal of seasoning. However, as my old army mess sergeant once said of Spam, it's cheap, and it's filling.

I exchanged some merchandise for three of the turtles, and we had the first for lunch that day. It was cooked in a five-gallon oil can. The men had cut a square hole on one side of the empty can, then had half-filled it with sand. Wood was placed on top of the sand and the fire lighted.

This primitive stove made it unnecessary for us to stop for our noon meal and thus saved us at least two hours a day.

That day, however, I was dozing when the cooking began, and when I awakened I was horrified to see that the men had turned one of the turtles upside down and placed it directly on top of the flames while alive.

It was still squirming when I awakened, but a few minutes later it was quiet; the body was loosened from the shell, and the men cut it into pieces and threw them into the cooking pot, which they placed on top of the can.

That day I smoked a cigar while the rest ate.

Late that afternoon we stopped at a desolate stretch of beach where the terecay turtles had laid their eggs.

On some beaches there are often as many as ten thousand eggs in a small area. They are round, about the size of a lemon, their shells white, tough, and elastic. Inside is a yellow yolk, but, instead of the white of a chicken egg, there is an oily substance which tastes like petroleum and never coagulates.

At dusk of a summer evening hundreds of female turtles, each about three feet long, go to a sandbank chosen by instinct and wait until just before dawn. Then they go to work. With their tails they dig a hole about three feet deep, deposit a few eggs in it, carefully put sand on top, lay another layer of eggs, cover it with a second thin layer of sand, and so on until the cavity is filled and hidden by the last layer of sand in such a way that only a trained eye can detect it.

That afternoon Simón dug a hundred and twenty-seven eggs out of a single hole, but in most of the others only about forty to sixty were found. I uncovered one in which there were seven recently hatched turtles, but, as soon as they were exposed to the light, they ran to the water and disappeared, probably to be immediately eaten by voracious fish.

Turtle hunting is not only a sport but also a major industry among the Indians and the town dwellers living along the Amazon and the Orinoco. In addition the eggs are eaten by certain kinds of birds and by jaguars. However, the terecay turtles not only survive but seem to increase in number every year.

The egg is usually boiled in salted water, which, since it penetrates the rubbery shell, seasons it at the same time. The oily substance is then thrown away. The yolk left tastes rather like chicken eggs. The eggs are also dried in the sun or made into a jelly seasoned with sugar and spices.

We must have picked up between three and four thousand eggs that afternoon, most of which were wasted when a few days later the men began pelting them at each other.

When they had finished they were covered with raw yolk and oil, and they all bathed themselves in the river. They said it had been a great game.

The small dugout I had sent ahead was waiting for us at Capihuara that evening, and I had planned to have three or four of the members of my crew paddle it until we reached the Cunu-cunuma River where, as I've explained, I had thought I could hire some Maquiritare Indians to take over the job.

However, just before we reached Capihuara, Teolo edged himself into the back of the large boat, where I was making some notes on the egg hunt.

"Señor Hector," he whispered, "last night, after you fell asleep, I heard the men say that if they have to paddle the small dugout, they will desert."

I was not surprised, but I decided that the only thing to do was to leave the small dugout in Capihuara.

At present the entire population of Capihuara consists of seven Baré Indian families, surrounded by rapidly disintegrating empty houses and the silent ghosts of a settlement that thrived when the rubber trade was flourishing.

Almost the minute I stepped off the boat one of the Barés—acutally, he was no more than one-third or one-fourth Indian—told me that a pious offering was to be made to one of the saints that night, and I was asked for a contribution of twenty bolívares —then worth about fifteen cents each.

The offering took place in a squalid little room with a dirt floor in which were half a dozen half-dressed young girls. The room was lighted by a single kerosene lamp, and in a niche on one wall was a tiny, cheap statue of the Virgin.

Candles were lighted under the statue as soon as I walked in, and an extremely brief prayer was said.

Then, to the music of a guitar and the usual pair of maracas, the drinking and dancing began. The fornication occurred a little later.

By midnight the guitarist, his tongue suitably loosened by the amount of *bureche* he had drunk, began a kind of calypso, which was lustily applauded at the end of each verse.

The song went on interminably, and I copied only a few of the verses:

Fué un alegre español
Que vino de Nueva York
Volando su propio avión
Que en San Carlos nos embarcó
Ay! Ay! Ay! Ay! La expedición
  guaharibera

There was a gay Spaniard
Who came from New York
Flying his own plane
Who in San Carlos embarked us
Ay! Ay! Ay! Ay! The expedition
  Guahariban

Al Alto Orinoco vamos
Con este loco español
Y dicen los que nos viceron
Que el cuerpo de puyas lleno
El guaica nos va a poner
Ay! Ay! Ay! Ay! La expedición
  guaharibera

To the Upper Orinoco we are
  going
With this crazy Spaniard
And the ones that saw us say
That the body full of arrows
The Guaica is going to fill us
Ay! Ay! Ay! Ay! The expedition
  Guahariban

El guaica y el guaharibo
A su mujer escondió
Del alegre español que vino
Y solo en la selva quedó
Con su botella de vino
Ay! Ay! Ay! Ay! La expedición
  guaharibera

The Guaica and the Guaharibo
His woman hid
From the gay Spaniard who came
And alone in the jungle he
  remained
With his bottle of wine
Ay! Ay! Ay! Ay! The expedition
  Guahariban

Manuel Padrón—who was nicknamed Chinchena—was an excellent guitarist but a totally incompetent crew member. The next morning, obviously suffering from a severe hangover, he and Simón got on the boat, one on each side, to take the day's food ration out of one of the aluminum containers.

All of a sudden, without warning, Chinchena jumped off the boat, leaving it unbalanced. Simón almost fell in the water, but steadied himself; instead the open container of food tumbled overboard, and most of the sugar for the entire expedition was lost. However, the beans, rice, lentils, and salt were taken out of the water and laid on the dock to dry. Since the sun was hot that day, they soon did.

Nevertheless, we had to put off our departure until the following morning. There was a second sacrifice to a saint that evening, and I was asked to make another contribution but declined.

However, late in the afternoon one of the crew members came to me to explain that two of his shirts which he said he had washed and hung on a bush to dry had been stolen. He obviously expected me to dig into the merchandise I had for trading with the Indians to replace them, but when I made no such offer he wandered away, muttering unpleasantly to himself. I was pretty sure that no shirts had been stolen; he simply wanted to sell some to buy bureche.

Despite my lack of co-operation he managed, as did all the other members of the crew, again excepting Severo and Teolo, to get roaring drunk anyway.

They were all in a stupor the next morning, but we started shortly after sunup, traveling all day and part of the night.

After we made camp the men threw half a dozen heavy fishhooks in the water; they were tied to a line which was secured to a tree. When we pulled out the hooks the next morning, all of them were not only empty but had been bent straight by the fish.

However, we had plenty of breakfast because two of the men

went hunting and within a few minutes had shot three *pavas*, large, meaty birds which are plentiful in the jungle and, roasted over an open fire, taste almost as good as domestic chicken, although the meat is tougher and stringier.

In addition Simón and Chinchena had spent an hour the evening before killing fish with machetes. The technique is not one of which any game warden would approve. They simply turned on flashlights, and, when the fish had emerged near the shore, struck them with their machetes.

As we ate we could see the majestic beauty of Mount Duida, black-purple against the cobalt blue of the sky. W. H. Hudson has described its particular magic so well that anyone else would be foolish to try. It is all in *Green Mansions,* a book I first read when I was nine and have reread on an average of once every year since. It is also one of the handful of books I usually take on my expeditions.

In another of Hudson's books, *The Purple Land,* there is a passage which I have typed out and keep, well hidden, of course, in one of the drawers of my desk in Bogotá.

Ah, yes, we are all vainly seeking after happiness in the wrong way. It was with us once and ours, but we despised it, for it was only the old common happiness which Nature gives to all her children, and we went away from it in search of another greater kind of happiness which some dreamer—Bacon or another—assured us we should find. We had only to conquer Nature, find out her secrets, make her our obedient slave, then the Earth would be Eden, and every man Adam and every woman Eve. We are still marching bravely on, conquering Nature, but how weary and sad we are getting! The old joy in life and gaiety of heart have vanished, though we do sometimes pause for a few minutes in our long forced march to watch the labours of some pale mechanism, seeking after perpetual motion, and indulge in a little dry, cackling laugh at his expense.

240

We navigated for another day, again until late in the evening and since the men had been complaining of fatigue we stopped at a spot called Pavón, where a large, irregular stone juts out of the water. I balanced my cot on a precariously narrow shelf of the rock and slept soundly, waking up only once, just in time to grab the ledge. I had turned over and was falling into the water.

Less than an hour after we were under way the next morning we entered the Orinoco.

At that moment the river was as impressive as the Mississippi. Its waters were a swirl of muddy yellow; it was at least two thousand feet across; the current was mild, and as soon as we entered the river we heard the playful gurgling snorts of three otters racing from one shore to another.

I could immediately see that, at the moment at least, my five-horsepower motor would have no trouble propelling the boat despite the fact that it was overloaded.

About half an hour later we arrived at Tama Tama, which is about a mile from the bifurcation of the Orinoco and the Casiquiare.

Tama Tama consists of a single weather-beaten house; the paint is peeling; it stands cold and naked-looking on the shore of the river, and when the creaking door with wooden bars opened, a strong-faced, white-haired woman emerged. She was Mrs. Flora Troxel, a Protestant missionary—Presbyterian, I believe—from the middle west of the U.S., who was living alone in the house just then. Her two colleagues, the Reverend Eugene Higdem and James Barker, were already among the Guaharibos, and Mrs. Troxel was getting ready to enter the jungle herself in a few days.

I liked her at once, and after she made me a cup of very strong tea we sat in the empty living room of the house for almost

241

an hour, talking about my expedition. Mrs. Troxel must have been in her late fifties or early sixties and has spent a good part of her life telling the Indians about the Christian God. She advised me against taking any Maquiritare Indians with me. The Guaharibos did not like them, she said, and there might be trouble. It would be better for us to go on alone.

She also said that a war had started on February 3 between the Guaicas of the Upper Siapa and those of the Orinoco, but she did not know if the fighting had ended or who was winning.

But she herself was not afraid. "I wish I could go with you," she said, "but for this year I am occupied with the Guaharibos. Next year, perhaps."

When I asked her if she ever got lonely, she smiled at me almost pityingly. "Of course not," she said. "I have no time for loneliness when I am engaged in the work of God." From someone else the words might have sounded false and foolish; coming from her, they were a simple statement of fact.

As we started up the river again she stood for a moment in the doorway, and her lips formed the words, "God bless you." Then she turned and closed the door. She did not watch us go. She was far too busy for that. Besides, she had told me, "I shall pray for you."

On the map of the Orinoco there is still a dot called Esmeralda, which was a flourishing mission at the time of the conquistadors.

At the time of the rubber boom Esmeralda briefly came to life again. A man named Colonel Pérez Franco homesteaded there, raising cattle and selling meat to the rubber traders. However, the traders drifted away, and one day the colonel had a disagreement with a Maquiritare, and the Indian in revenge got in touch with the Guaharibos.

Two days later Esmeralda was attacked; the colonel's belongings were stolen and his cattle killed. He and his family were spared, but he was financially ruined, and he returned to Puerto Ayacucho.

Now there is only jungle marked "unexplored" on the map. Esmeralda has again been abandoned, and all that is left is a grove of now-wild lemon trees once cultivated by the Spaniards.

From Esmeralda, Mount Duida was even more impressive. Its summit was obscured by clouds, but beneath could be seen the edges of an immense plateau. Just to the right was a group of granite hills no more than three or four hundred feet in height.

The morning after our arrival I made an excursion along the tops of the hills, returning just before dusk. Here the plains of Duida seem near enough to touch. In every direction the vast carpet of tall grass which begins there, broken occasionally by a neat grove of palm trees, spreads to the edge of the river. Far in the distance was a huge silver lake in which I could see capybaras and alligators swimming together. Looking toward the Upper Orinoco, I dimly saw a range of black-purple mountain peaks, the Sierra Parima, and beyond that only the immense blue of the almost cloudless sky.

From Esmeralda on there is an abrupt change from the semi-civilized to the completely primitive. The Orinoco is bordered by rolling hills, and there are large sandy beaches on both sides of the gradually narrowing river. In addition there are alligators, tapirs, turtles, and dozens of varieties of brightly colored birds and monkeys of all sizes. The animals came down to the river to drink and watched us undisturbed. They had never heard the sound of a hunter's gun.

I had already warned the men not to fire in case we were attacked by Indians. I felt sure that, even if they were belligerent at first, we could quiet them with presents, and I did not want them to think we had come to make war on them. That would have been fatal. Our party was so small we would have had no chance to fight back.

Several afternoons we stopped on the beaches and gathered more turtle eggs, always being careful to avoid the hundreds of rays which were everywhere.

I always carry at least a dozen morphine injections in my medicine kit for use in case of ray sting. Potassium permanganate and chewed tobacco are helpful, and some tribes believe that if a menstruating virgin sits on the wound, the pain will disappear.

By nightfall we had already seen the signs of the Guaharibo tribes, a few palm-leaf structures of the most primitive nature, used only for overnight stops. They might indicate that our presence had already been detected. There was no way of knowing, and there was nothing to do except go on. But some members of my crew were already muttering discontentedly.

Pablo Guimará—who was called "Mará"—said he had dealt with the Guaharibos several years before when he was taking timber out of the area surrounding Esmeralda.

One afternoon, he said, a group of Guaharibos appeared at the lumber camp, apparently on a friendly visit. However, everyone was frightened, and the Indians were immediately given all the gifts available. In return, the Guaharibos presented the whites with their bows and arrows.

For a time, everything went well; then one of the Guaharibos picked up a fishline and started to walk off with it. One of the lumbermen, "the youngest," said Mará, "and the most foolish," objected and grabbed the fishline away.

"Immediately," said Mara, "how I do not know, all the Indians had a branch or a stick in their hands. They started to attack us, and we avoided trouble only by giving them more gifts.

"I was much afraid, however. It is an experience I do not wish again to have. But I did learn that the Guaharibos are afraid of firearms, mostly because of the noise they make.

"If they begin stealing our possessions, the best way to protect them is to place our guns on those things we wish to keep. They will not move them."

The men nodded nervously and said nothing. It would have taken very little for them to have fled in panic.

Actually I'm not sure Mará was telling the truth; he may never have seen a Guaharibo. He claimed to have an intimate knowledge of the Upper Orinoco, but I think he lied. He had never been there before.

All of us slept fitfully that night, expecting at any moment to be surrounded by Indians, but the only attacks were from mosquitoes, which were so numerous that after a few seconds without being covered by a net Severo was a mass of blood-clotted bites. In addition I was bitten on the hand and on the top of the head by a wasp.

It was a miserable night, and when we started out again the next morning all of us were irritable.

However, the dawn was clear and cool, and in a little while Chinchena was singing one of his endless songs, about tapirs and about monkeys and rays and virgins. We all joined him on the "Ay! Ay! Ay! Ay!" with which he began the last line of each verse.

In midmorning we passed the mouths of the Padámo and Ocámo tributaries, and once, when Simón shot down a bird, its body had already been half eaten by the piranhas when we lifted it out of the water. An hour or so later Mará shot a huge tapir swimming across the bow of our boat; in the less than a minute

245

and a half before we got it into the dugout, its foot and part of a leg had disappeared.

At this point the waters of the Orinoco were low, and the river began to narrow rapidly. In some places it was no more than one hundred feet across, at others twice again that wide. The thick jungle undergrowth came to the very edges of the river, but the current remained mild, the water a muddy yellow-brown.

We went on that night until after eight, always hoping that around the next bend we would find a wide spot of sandy beach, preferably on the right bank of the river.

I felt that if the war Mrs. Troxel had warned us about was still going on, the hostile forces would be coming up the left bank, since the attackers were tribes of the Upper Siapa. What's more, by this time we were fairly sure that we were surrounded.

Of course, it was possible that by some miracle we had not been seen, but it was difficult to understand how we could have gone all through the Guaharibo territory and have entered the area occupied by the Guaicas without a single encounter with an Indian. There seemed to be only two possible explanations: one, that the Indians were all away from the Orinoco, counterattacking the Siapa tribes, or that we were being carefully observed from the dark density of the jungle and that an attack on us was planned.

At any moment I expected to hear the angry shouts of a mob of Guaicas. I was certain they had heard our motor by now.

However, just in case, that day I refused to allow the men to shoot any of the birds that were so temptingly poised on the branches of trees, leaning far over into the water.

The sound of a gun being fired was bound to attract attention.

We finally settled for the night on the right bank of an unnamed tributary of the river and, after we had moored the boat, the men cleared with their machetes enough space for us to hang our hammocks.

Again nothing happened in the uneasy hours between darkness and dawn.

Early the next morning we were followed for more than an hour by a trio of female *toninas* or manatees, which are also sometimes called cowfish. They are shaped like sea lions, but instead of fur on their blue-black bodies have patches of coarse hair. Their mouths are like those of cows, and, since they are not really fish at all but mammals, their food consists of grass, which they shyly nibble on the banks of rivers. They get around in the water by means of a pair of flippers and broad, flat tails.

The manatees are responsible for the legends about mermaids because of their breasts, which, from a distance, resemble those of women. At least some people say they do. I disagree. At feeding time the female manatees hold their babies between their flippers, and the breasts, when pressed, yield a white milk which is said to be bitter and rather oily in taste.

The Indians treat the manatees with reverence, partly because of their strength. Although they are seldom more than eight feet long, they frequently battle alligators—and invariably win. What's more, the Indians insist that if a man falls out of his dugout and is seen by a manatee, he will be slapped to shore by its flippers and tail.

The laws of Venezuela forbid shooting manatees. The Indians frequently capture them in strong nets placed across the entrance to their feeding places, or harpoon them. The flesh is said to taste like a cross between pork and beef. The oil from the fat with which their bodies are covered is used to cure all kinds of ills, real and imagined.

247

That night we slept only about twenty yards from the river, and as we were making camp we noticed for the first time a clearly defined Indian path with fresh tracks on it.

This made it almost certain that we would see some Guaicas the next day—possibly before dawn.

The men began to panic immediately; even Severo and Teolo were nervous. In addition to my own uneasiness I had a fever and a cough, the result of smoking a cigar Simón had lent me. He had had a slight cold a few days before, and, since I did not see him wash his hands from the start of the expedition until the end, it is not surprising that he transmitted the germs to me on the cigar. What's more, I had been eating very little and smoking a good deal during the last two or three days. My lips were painfully blistered.

Nevertheless, I pretended to be delighted with the camp site we had found; I carefully examined the Indian tracks and said that they were unquestionably a week or more old, which was ridiculous. The only expert on Indian tracks I've ever come across, in books or in life, is the Deerslayer, and I share Mark Twain's low opinion of the works of James Fenimore Cooper.

Just for the hell of it, though, I told the men, not that it was at all necessary, that we'd hang our hammocks in a circle and take our baggage out of the boat and place it in the center. I ordered two men to spend the night in the boat. They started to protest, but when I whirled on them angrily they quietly padded down to the river.

By this time my forehead was blazing, and once I nearly fainted with fatigue.

I told the men to get a good night's rest because we'd probably see our first Indians in the morning—and I predicted that the Guaicas would be delighted with our gifts.

Then I undressed, as I always do at night in the jungle or anywhere else, lay down in my hammock, rolled myself in a blanket, and began to shake with a chill.

The men were still talking in low whispers and then, without warning, were silent. There had been a rustling in the jungle only a few steps away.

I, too, was holding my breath when two large monkeys jumped from one tree to another just over our heads.

After that the men remained quiet, and I listened for their regular breathing but heard none. No one was asleep.

It was nearly five in the morning when I dozed off. My timing could not have been worse. If there had been an attack, it almost certainly would have been just before dawn.

I slept for about two hours, during which time I dreamed that we were surrounded by Indians wearing what appeared to be mink coats, followed by a character in a coonskin cap who looked very much like the Deerslayer. The Indians were friendly enough, but the Deerslayer didn't seem to like me, and he picked up an ax and was about to chop off my head when I awakened covered with a cold sweat. However, my cold was gone.

I roused the men, which was easy enough since most of them were only half asleep, and after some coffee we started up the river again.

The date was March 3. It had been exactly fourteen days since we had left San Carlos and San Felipe, and I was sure that before sundown we would meet up with the Guaicas.

The air was hot and heavy with the odor of a cloying jungle flower. From somewhere deep in the jungle there was the smell of death, an animal, I'm sure, but just then I would have sworn it was human. The sun was an unrelenting red ball of flame, and the men, their bodies dripping sweat, lay listlessly on the boxes and parcels. No one spoke. Chinchena's guitar lay neglected at his side, and when someone mockingly growled out an "Ay! Ay!" he responded with a brief, appropriate obscenity.

The river seemed to be drying up as we watched; there was almost no current, and the only sound was the murmur of the motor and the rhythmic snore of Severo, who lay at my feet, his huge head on Teolo's chest.

An hour passed and then another and a third, and it was time for lunch, but no one stirred.

Once Simón relieved himself by the side of the boat, and again Chinchena asked me for a cigar, but when I told him to take one out of the proper cylinder, he shook his head lazily.

Around one I had closed my eyes, and I may even have been sleeping when it happened, when a cry—more a scream, really— rang out from the right bank of the river, filled the air for a moment, real and terrible and terrifying.

I leapt to my feet. The other members of the crew were already standing upright in the middle of the boat, tense and unmoving.

After that there was silence for what could have been a second or a minute or five.

Then the cry was repeated, louder this time and closer and higher in pitch.

The men turned to me, and I knew without looking that Severo was watching me. I cleared my throat, then cleared it again, and finally shouted back.

A series of undecipherable screams followed, and as they continued I think all of us were prepared for a fusillade of arrows. Simón raised one hand above his head, as if to ward off a blow.

Finally, what might have been a human voice, and might have been the cry of an animal from further inside the jungle, seemed to answer the shouting onshore.

After that there was silence again, and none of us was really breathing.

A few seconds later there was a rustling sound; the tall vegetation parted, and the figure of a man appeared through the tangle of dark green which was everywhere along the shore.

His appearance was by no means impressive. He was short and had a thin body; his forehead slanted alarmingly, and he was completely nude. He carried half a dozen very long arrows and a bow that was nearly as tall as he was.

He continued to shout at someone in the jungle behind him. Then he looked at us, jumped up and down a couple of times, and began pointing excitedly up the river.

That moment was, I think, the most exciting of any expedition I've been on before or since.

"I think," I said to Severo after a long pause, "that we have found a friend."

The huge Jívaro grinned at me. "Must not get much to eat up this way," he said, indicating the thin body of the nude Indian.

Teolo was almost falling out of the boat in excitement, and the rest of the crew had started breathing again.

For perhaps five minutes I took pictures of the Guaica, both movies and stills, and then I motioned for Simón, who just then was in charge of the motor, to get as close to the Indian as possible, then, no matter what, rapidly head toward the middle of the river again.

"When we go by him," I told Severo, "you grab him and pull him into the boat."

Chinchena muttered something about its not being safe to take a savage on board, but I ignored him, even though I had no idea whether there were any or a hundred others hiding on shore.

However, as soon as we neared the shore, the Indian held out his hand and, with Severo's help, jumped aboard, grinning and shouting.

"*Shoree Nohee!*" he said, and then repeated, "*Shoree Nohee!*"

After that he carefully put down his bow and arrows, seated himself between Severo and me, and began patting and stroking us.

"*Shoree Nohee!*" he said again, and it was not necessary to understand Guaica to know that he was saying we were his friends.

I took a piece of paper and a pencil out of my pocket and drew a group of crude huts, then by signs asked the direction of the Guaica village.

Our passenger nodded violently but pointed nowhere; so we continued upriver.

I gently placed a cigarette in his mouth and, after demonstrating how to smoke it, lighted it for him. However, within seconds it was so wet with saliva that it disintegrated, and he contemptuously threw the remains over the side of the boat, then opened his wide, full-lipped mouth and took a roll of tobacco leaves about the size of a cigar from between the gum and the inside of his lower lip.

He carefully smoothed the roll of tobacco and offered it to me, grinning foolishly. He had the face of a monkey, particularly with the tobacco in his mouth.

I smiled kindly at him and shook my head, hurriedly lighting a cigar to avoid his offering me his tobacco a second time.

I opened the thermos and poured some hot coffee in a cup, first drinking a little myself, then handing it to him. He took a mouthful, rinsed it around inside his mouth, made a wry face, and spat it overboard.

At that point, I took a mirror, a comb, and a machete from the pile of merchandise and handed them to him. He looked at himself in the mirror and chortled, but when I showed him how to use the comb he did not seem interested.

However, he continued patting me on the back, smiling and repeating, "Shoree Nohee!"

No more than fifteen or twenty minutes later there was another shrill cry from somewhere inside the jungle. Our passenger half rose in his seat and yelled back his answer.

The screaming conversation continued for a few minutes, after which three more Guaicas appeared onshore, all nude, all carrying bows and arrows, all shouting. They stood for a moment on a fallen tree trunk, and I had Simón maneuver the boat toward them, but only two jumped aboard.

The third ran off into the jungle, probably to warn the village of our arrival.

I gave the two new arrivals the same three gifts, and they exchanged mirrors, gurgling with pleasure at the sight of each other's faces and chattering amiably. I realized that they might be telling each other that as soon as they got us to their settlement they would chop off our heads with the machetes, but I doubted it.

As we continued around a bend in the river, we saw the first Guaica bridge. The construction could not have been more simple. First, heavy poles had been tied together in an x shape, and these were placed at regular intervals across the bed of the river. Then other poles, really no more than thick logs, were placed horizontally on the crutches formed by the first. Finally two lighter logs were tied above the crutch to form handrails.

Building such bridges would seem to be an easy matter where the water is shallow and the river no more than about a hundred and fifty yards across, but I'm sure they could not be constructed in places where the water is deep and the river wide. I imagine, too, that most of them are washed away during the rainy season.

However, they are necessary to the Guaicas because, as I later discovered, they have never learned how to build dugouts.

On the right bank of the river immediately beyond the first bridge stood a group of fifty naked Guaicas, all male. They watched our approach in complete silence.

I told Simón to take the boat close to shore once more, to let me out with our three passengers, and then to turn quickly and go to the middle of the river where a large tree trunk jutted out of the water.

"No, Señor Hector," said Severo. "It is not safe for you to go alone. You are only one man against many. I will go with you."

"I'll be all right," I told him. "Besides, I don't want the boat invaded and all of our equipment stolen or upset."

"No," Severo repeated doggedly. "I will go with you."

I shook my head and said, "You stay here. That's an order."

The Jívaro's face fell, but he seated himself again, and the three Guaicas and I leapt off the boat and onto the beach. The dugout turned around and quickly chugged toward the tree trunk.

For a moment no one spoke. Then I pointed toward the narrow path leading into the jungle and, by signs, indicated that I wanted to be taken to the village.

The older men looked at me apprehensively and began talking among themselves, some of them shouting. Others examined my beard, stroked my head, unbuttoned my shirt, pulled up my trouser legs and clapped their hands with wonder when they saw my woolen red socks emerging from the tops of my leather boots. One muscular young man indicated he wanted me to give the socks and boots to him, but I shivered vigorously, indicating that, without socks, I would surely freeze. Once I placed my wrist watch against the ear of one of the older men and immediately regretted it because I spent the better part of the next few days stretching out my arm while someone listened to my watch tick.

Finally a middle-aged man who appeared to be a leader said, "*Shoree Nohee!*" He walked over to me and patted my head.

"*Shoree Nohee!*" he repeated, and the others said it after him.

Then the leader started up the path, and I followed, the rest falling in after me, single file, since the path itself was only about a foot wide. Every fifty yards or so a branch had been placed across it, obviously so that if the village was attacked the noise made by the cracking of the branches would warn of the invaders' approach.

After about fifteen minutes we arrived at the village. I had never before seen anything so primitive and probably never will again.

The clearing, which was completely hidden by a thick blanket of branches which the leader pushed aside to allow me to enter, was no more than a hundred yards in diameter and was bare of vegetation. The thirty or more shelters were nothing more than the inclined frames of roofs, covered with palm leaves which almost reached the ground. Some of the shelters were so close together that they met; others were separated by a space the width of a man. Three sides of the house were open, the slanting roof serving as the fourth wall.

I had already noticed that the arrows the men carried were pointed with hard woods and animal bones rather than metal, another indication of the savage state of the Guaicas. Their shelters also showed that they were seminomadic.

I examined the houses, admiring them noisily, repeating,

255

"*Shoree Nohee!*" at appropriate intervals, and keeping my eyes open for women. I saw none.

Finally, after first trying, not very successfully, to explain my plans, I walked back toward the river, followed by most of the men.

Simón brought the boat to shore again, but the Guaicas did not crowd around it. They seemed to be afraid.

I gave my instructions quickly and helped Teolo take out enough equipment to last the two of us for three days, as well as some gifts.

After that I told Severo to go with the other men across river and make camp there. I would have preferred to have him with me, but did not trust the others alone, and I wanted to keep the crew and the Guaicas apart. Besides, I had noticed that the bridge was broken; so there was no way for the Indians to cross to the other side.

After Teolo and I had unloaded our supplies and gifts, he stepped ashore, and the boat chugged off across the river, Severo sadly watching us from the rear.

As the Guaicas crowded around us, I vigorously patted Teolo on the back, shouted, "*Shoree Nohee!*" a few times, and then divided the parcels up among the many who wanted to help carry them.

When we got back to the settlement, Teolo and I were given an unoccupied shelter, and I hung my hammock. The entire male population of the village stood outside and watched everything we did, exclaiming over the brightly colored hammock, fondling the gasoline stove, gasping at our food supply, and grinning with the wonder of my flashlight.

Once or twice I thought I saw an elderly woman in the background, but when I would turn for a better look one of the men would have stepped in front to hide my view.

It was not until the next day that I learned why. Since the Guaicas, like other primitive tribes, fight most of their wars over women, they were understandably suspicious of me. As soon as they heard of our approach, they hid all except a few of the oldest women in the jungle.

The Guaicas are a thin, muscular people who seem to average about five feet four in height. Since they spend almost all of their time in the depths of the jungle and seldom expose themselves to the sun, their skins are light, so much so that they are probably the famous "lost white Indians," who have been part of the legend of the Orinoco since the time of the conquistadors.

Both sexes are nude except for a thin string of animal skin or interwoven palm fibers around their middles. The men tie their foreskins to this string, which thus holds the penis erect. In addition some of the women wear a somewhat heavier string of fibers across their chests.

The men and women both wear their hair in a manner resembling that adopted by the order of Franciscans, shaved close on top and cut short above their ears. The women have a small hole bored on each side of their lips and a third underneath, through which they place small wooden sticks as ornaments. Most of them also wear slightly larger nose sticks and earrings made of flowers.

A few of the men have perforations under their lips into which they insert feathers.

All the adults paint flamboyant patterns on their faces with a purple vegetable dye, and they wear arm bands decorated with flowers, leaves, and feathers as well as necklaces made of seeds and thin bands of twisted fiber above their ankles, below their knees, and on their wrists. All except the very young also have the roll of tobacco between the gum and the inside of the lower lip. The roll is often passed from person to person as a gesture of friendship, and I was offered several but managed to have a cigar in my mouth most of the time so that I could politely decline. Teolo was not so lucky.

The Guaicas eat a great many bananas, of which they cultivate at least six varieties, ranging in size from those somewhat smaller than are available in the U.S. to giant yellow fruit more than a foot and a half in length. They also eat the flesh of wild animals and fish, sometimes cooked, sometimes raw. They make their fires by rubbing two wooden sticks together; the women weave simple baskets in which the food is served, and the men get themselves drunk by using a narcotic, the origin of which I never discovered. When under its influence, they pace up and down in front of their shelters, chanting an unintelligible song which may have a religious meaning. They know nothing about the wonders of alcohol.

Most of the men have long, deep scars on the tops of their heads, and at first I thought these were the result of tribal wars. I learned later that they were simply the marks of matrimony.

In general all of the women are used indiscriminately by all of the men, but if a man wants his own woman, he has to pass a matrimonial test of fitness. The girl's father strikes him hard on top of the head three times with a heavy wooden stick made razor-sharp along one edge.

When the test is over the prospective bridegroom's head is bloody, but it must also be unbowed. Otherwise he is not considered worthy of having a woman for himself.

Both Teolo and I slept the clock around during our first day and night with the Guaicas, and on our second day we were besieged by even more visitors than on our first, men and now old women who wanted to lie on my hammock, try on my helmet, taste my food, or just run their fingers through my beard. They recognized Teolo as a fellow Indian and paid much less attention to him.

In the afternoon I went completely around the perimeter of the clearing, stopping at every lean-to for a short conversation in sign language. I did this to gain the Guaicas' confidence, and I felt I was successful, because during the afternoon of our third day in Mahakodo Tedi, as they called their village, I saw five pairs of bright, intent brown eyes staring at me from the bushes to one side of my shelter.

I half closed my own eyes, pretending to sleep, and in a little while, one light-skinned, grinning, nude girl emerged, looked at me curiously, moved forward a few steps, and softly called to her companions.

Then four other girls, one of them with a magnificent figure, stepped out of the bushes and stood watching me, commenting at length on my appearance.

I opened my eyes cautiously and slowly began to raise myself from my hammock.

But the girls were gone.

About half an hour later, while I was talking, again in sign language, to half a dozen elderly men, the girls came out of the jungle a second time. One of the men shouted something at them, and they timidly came forward until they were just outside the shelter.

I reached into one of the parcels and took out five mirrors, carefully handing one to each of the girls. They grabbed them and ran back to their hiding places, but I felt then that the Guaicas were no longer suspicious of me.

By that time I had decided to remain alone in Mahakodo Tedi for at least a week, during which I hoped to be able to persuade a party of men to go with me to the source of the river, which I felt could not be too far away.

However, I felt I had to be alone, and I told Teolo, who was disappointed and a little angry. He, too, had seen the girls.

We went down to the beach, and I shouted to the men.

When they had crossed the river, I took out enough provisions to last an additional seven days plus a few more gifts. Then Teolo got aboard, and I told Severo to take the crew down river about thirty miles. In a week, I said, the boat should return to pick me up. At that time I hoped we could continue our journey to the headwaters of the river the Guaicas call Balawa Mahakado.

Severo shook his head doubtfully as I explained that I knew the Indians had at least two guards watching the boat night and day, and I had seen other men go down to the river to swim across so that they could find out what the crew was up to.

This seemed to me to mean that, while the Guaicas accepted me, they would not bring the women out of the jungle or agree to accompany me for the rest of the journey unless I was alone with them for a while.

"I do not like this," said Severo, but he transmitted my orders to the men.

Then, just as the boat was about to turn around to go down river, we heard the startling, the unbelievable purr of a second motor. At first I thought the sound was only an echo of our own five-horsepower motor, but as the noise grew in intensity I realized that another, larger boat was approaching.

A few seconds later a huge launch roared around the bend in the river, and I saw a small, erect figure waving at me from the bow.

As the launch churned nearer a familiar voice shouted, "Señor Acebes! Greetings!"

Then I recognized the figure as that of Don Manuel Azavache, the prefect of San Carlos, who had wanted to accompany me on my expedition, but had not because he felt he was thirty years too old.

I had thought so too, but here he was, a distance from San Carlos that had taken me fourteen days to reach.

I smiled and waved back, but even then I was sure something was wrong. At that moment I had a feeling that the expedition was over.

"How are you, Don Manuel?" I shouted back. "It is good to see you," but my voice lacked conviction.

There were five other men in the launch, two policemen in faded khaki and three Indians. As the launch drew up in front of me, all five seemed to try to avoid my eyes.

However, Don Manuel grinned and pumped my hand.

"You are too thin," he said, "but you are also brown. You look well."

By this time a few Guaicas were crowding around the boat, but the majority were waiting silently in the background. The air was tense with excitement but also with the feeling of fear. The Guaicas had apparently not been afraid of one medium-sized boat with a five-horsepower motor, but here was a ten-ton launch with a seventy-five-horsepower motor.

There were also six additional men aboard, each a source of possible trouble.

The powerful, middle-aged leader stood in front of the others, watching us through narrowed eyes. I noticed also that a dozen or more of the younger men carried their bows and arrows for the first time in three days.

I told Don Manuel that he, too, looked well. "But what," I said, keeping my voice calm, "brings you up this far?"

The old man shook his head mournfully and pulled me away from the others.

"There is trouble, Señor Acebes," he said. "Serious trouble. I hesitate even to tell you."

I felt the color drain from my face, and I placed my hand on Don Manuel's shoulder.

"Go ahead, Don Manuel," I said. "You must tell me."

"Well," he began, "a little after you left a telegram arrived from Caracas saying to hold you until a commission of two men arrived to interview you.

"Since you were gone, I naturally wired back saying so.

"Two days later I received a second telegram saying that the two men were coming anyway.

"I immediately left San Carlos to head them off, feeling that their trip would be a waste of time and of money. I met them late that afternoon, they in their launch, I in mine, and I told them that you had departed for the Upper Orinoco.

"They flew into a rage, demanding to know why I had allowed you to go, and, when I said that your papers were in order, one of them, a Doctor Cruxent coming from Caracas, said many things which I do not wish to repeat. The other man, a Señor José Ángel Vargas, is the prefect of San Fernando de Atabapo, and he, too, said words that one man should not say of another."

Don Manuel sadly shrugged his rounded shoulders.

"This Doctor Cruxent immediately ordered me to find you and bring you back to San Carlos. He said that he must see you and that he must examine your papers."

"But why," I demanded, my voice rising, "why do they want to see my papers? You are the government authority in San Carlos, and you have approved them."

"That is true," said Don Manuel, looking everywhere but at

me. "I asked this Doctor Cruxent to come with me if he did not believe me, but he refused. He said you must return, and he is of the government in Caracas."

"On what authority does he make demands?" I shouted. "Who the hell is he, anyway?"

"He is," said Don Manuel, "a doctor, but I do not believe he cures the sick. He does not seem to me the kind of man who would do that."

"Well," I said firmly, "I'm not going back."

I could see fear in Don Manuel's eyes, and I immediately changed my mind. He was a fine man, but he was afraid, and I knew that if I did not return to San Carlos with him, he would be in serious trouble.

"All right," I said, shrugging, my voice no more than a whisper, "I shall return with you."

He took my hand in his and held it tight for a moment, then turned and went aboard the launch again.

As I ordered Severo to tie our dugout to the launch, he looked questioningly at me but said nothing. He seemed to sense what had happened, and so did the Guaicas.

When I went back to Mahakodo Tedi to pack my belongings, the Indians stood silently outside the shelter, not even whispering among themselves. After I had packaged everything half a dozen men quietly stooped and picked up the parcels.

A few minutes later as I climbed into the launch, the leader raised his hand and shouted, "*Shoree Nohee!*" and the others repeated it after him, all of them, the men in the foreground, and the women, who had appeared in a body for the first time, shouting from the edge of the jungle.

I looked back at Severo, but he had his eyes on the river. Teolo, who after he saw the five girls had carefully adjusted his sombrero every time he put it on, had jammed it down over his ears and was frowning.

However, the rest of my crew was happy, and Chinchena was singing some foolish song about the joys of going down instead of up the Orinoco and about all the girls who would consent to go to bed with him the second he got back to San Carlos.

"Ay! Ay!" he began, and I leaned back and shouted, "Shut the hell up."

"Ay!" he began again, then closed his mouth tight.

After that there was only the roar of the seventy-five-horse-power motor.

Since the launch had such a powerful motor, it took us only half as long to go down the Orinoco as it had to journey upward toward its source. We arrived in San Carlos in seven days.

The weather was beautiful all the way, the sun shining gently down, a soft breeze blowing across the bow of the boat most of the time, a nearly full moon every night, and for much of the way the wonder of Duida in the background. But I scarcely noticed.

I cursed. I sulked. I slept. I ate, and, when I could, I read from *Green Mansions*, this time with especial emphasis on Hudson's description of the government that was forcing me back from my nearly completed expedition.

Both of us may be prejudiced, but his words seem to me as apropos as when he wrote them:

Every nation, someone remarks, has the government it deserves, and Venezuela certainly has the one it deserves and that suits it best. We call it a republic, not only because it is not one, but also because a thing must have a name; and to have a good name, or a fine name, is very convenient—especially when you want to borrow money. If the Venezuelans, thinly distributed over an area of half a million square

264

miles, mostly illiterate peasants, half-breeds, and indigenes, were educated, intelligent men, zealous only for the public weal, it might be
possible for them to have a real republic. They have instead a government of cliques, tempered by revolution; and a very good government
it is, in harmony with the physical conditions of the country and the
national temperament . . .

I could not understand why I was being brought back from an
expedition which men, including Venezuelans, had dreamed of
making for centuries. I had been given every paper I needed by
the Venezuelan Embassy in Bogotá, with the exception of a gun
permit, which I received from Cabo Perales, the commander of
La Guardia Nacional in San Carlos. And now a Doctor Cruxent,
who did not cure people, and a Señor Vargas were having me
hauled back, no more, I was certain, than a hundred miles from
my goal.

I was sure of that because the morning before leaving
Mahakodo Tedi I had climbed a steep, three-peaked hill behind
the village. The Guaicas call the hill Tabashiua, and from one of
its peaks I had seen the Sierra Parima, no more than ninety miles
away.

As I told Don Manuel, "That means a trip of no more than
twenty days to reach the headwaters and much less than that if
the river can be navigated.

"It is absolutely insane to be going backward when I was so
near."

Don Manuel smiled philosophically. "I know, I know," he said,
"but such is the way of life."

"Such," I replied, "is the way of Venezuela."

Later I was sorry I had spoken so harshly, and I apologized. I
was fond of Don Manuel, and most of the Venezuelans I met
were kindly, gentle people. There were and are two outstanding
exceptions.

A little above San Felipe and San Carlos, Severo, with Don Manuel's permission, untied the dugout, and we went on to San Felipe in Colombia. Don Manuel docked across the river in San Carlos, Venezuela.

Roberto Londoño was waiting for me at the dock, standing next to a squat, dark man wearing enormous horn-rimmed glasses, badly in need of a haircut, and with the enormous belly of an inveterate beer drinker. His small eyes, which the glasses magnified, were rimmed with red, and when I stepped on the dock he stumbled as he walked forward.

I knew the reason from his breath.

"Well," he said, extending his limp, white hand, the nails of which were rimmed with black, and then he repeated, "Well.

"I am Señor Vargas," he went on, his eyes noting my haggard face and the fact that my clothes fitted me loosely.

I shook his hand briskly.

"A difficult trip, yes?" he asked.

"Very," I said, "and now I want to know what kind of joke this is. Why was I brought back here?"

Señor Vargas swayed, and he smiled loosely but said nothing. Then, as the crew started to bring my luggage ashore, he began pacing up and down in front of the headquarters house. He looked at me and started to speak but changed his mind. Finally he called to Londoño and whispered something to him.

After a few minutes Londoño returned to my side. "The señor," he said, "is convinced you are breaking the law. He says that since you sailed from San Carlos you should have docked there now so that he could examine your baggage."

I snorted. "Why?" I demanded. "He's got no jurisdiction on the Río Negro. He's prefect of a little village somewhat larger than San Carlos, and that's all. Don Manuel is in charge here, and he gave me permission to land at San Felipe."

By this time my voice had risen, and Señor Vargas turned toward me for a moment, then away.

"He says you may have a lot of contraband in your luggage," Londoño went on, "and he even claims you may have some diamonds picked up on the expedition."

"Damn it," I said. "I've got exactly what I started out with, and the Venezuelan Embassy in Bogotá has a list in triplicate. Señor Vargas can get the information he wants from his own government, not from me."

I started walking toward Vargas, my fists clenched, and he immediately trotted to his boat, stepped in, and started across the river.

He did not once glance back.

For the next half hour I was too busy helping unload my own boat to worry about Vargas and Cruxent, but shortly after we had finished and I had bathed and changed my clothes I heard the put-put of an outboard motor.

I glanced out the window and saw Vargas sitting in a boat, the inevitable bottle of beer in his hand. Beside him was a thin blond man of perhaps forty. He had wide blue eyes and clean-cut features and, in a movie juvenile way, might have been considered handsome.

As the boat docked and he stood up, I saw that he was a foot shorter than I, and I changed my mind about hitting Cruxent immediately.

I walked outside, and the blond man came forward, his hand extended.

"Doctor Acebes?" he asked.

I neither spoke nor nodded.

"I am," he went on, his voice that of a man who has listened to himself and found the sound pleasant, "Doctor José Cruxent.

As you probably know I am director of the Museum of Natural Science in Caracas."

I didn't move a muscle.

"I am, again as you probably know," he went on, giving me a smile he had probably used with a good deal of success with many women, "an anthropologist."

His hand was still extended, and he pushed it toward me.

I seemed not to see it.

The doctor looked at me for a moment longer, then carefully placed the hand in the pocket of his jacket. A vein throbbed in the forehead of his unlined face. He waited, Vargas standing a little behind him, trying to hide the half-empty bottle of beer behind his back.

Finally I spoke. "What do you want of me, Cruxent?" I asked.

The doctor's eyes widened, and he looked at me with the innocence of a child unfairly accused of stealing a cooky.

"Want of you?" he said, bewilderment in his voice. "I want nothing of you, sir. Nothing at all." He spoke with a slight French accent.

"Then why the hell did you make me return?" I asked.

Cruxent's thin lips spread away from his extremely white teeth in an excellent imitation of a smile.

"You must be mistaken," he said. "I didn't make you return."

"You told Don Manuel Azavache to bring me back," I said.

He shook the handsome head back and forth a couple of times. "I told him no such thing," he said firmly.

"You must be mistaken," he repeated.

I knew Don Manuel well enough to be sure he was not lying, but Cruxent's effrontery was so bold that I couldn't think of a word to say.

The doctor removed his hand from his jacket, took a cigarette, carefully tapped it with the tip of one neatly manicured finger, and lit it with what could have been a silver lighter.

He blew the smoke through his nose, then said, "Doctor Acebes, when I heard of the expedition of a Colombian I did think it very strange that I was not familiar with your work, because I have many scientific colleagues in Bogotá as well as most of the other capitals of the world.

"So I decided to come down to talk to you. That is all."

"I'll be damned," I said. "You've had me brought all the way back here for a little tête-à-tête. I'm touched, Cruxent."

"Besides," the doctor went on as if he had not heard me, "all expeditions into Venezuela pass through Caracas, and I certainly thought it strange that you hadn't looked me up."

"Look," I said, "I can enter Venezuela through any place where there is a government authority, like San Carlos. It was easier for me to come here, and I did. The Venezuelan Embassy in Bogotá gave me permission.

"If you wanted to chat with me, you should have come with Don Manuel. I'm not in the habit of having people send policemen to pick me up."

The doctor flicked an ash to the ground. He gave me the brilliant smile again.

"The whole incident," he said, "is most regrettable."

"You're damned right it's regrettable," I said.

He dropped the cigarette and smashed it with the heel of a black, neatly shined shoe.

Señor Vargas, who had been silently nursing his beer in the background, threw the empty bottle into the river. then said drunkenly, "There is obviously complicity here."

"What the hell do you mean?" I asked.

Vargas did not reply.

"Look," I said, "I'll take this up with the Venezuelan Embassy in Bogotá." I started away, then turned back again.

"But meantime," I said, "I want to know who's going to pay me the 12,000 pesos I've already invested in this expedition."

"Do you mean," Cruxent asked, "that you don't work for a museum or a scientific society? Is this your own enterprise?"

I nodded. "And I paid for it myself," I said.

The doctor's face broke into what was this time a genuine smile of relief. "Oh," he said. "I see."

He picked up the cigarette and scattered the ashes, Army fashion.

"Come," he said to Vargas, "it is time for us to be getting back to San Carlos."

Then, without another word, he and the prefect of San Fernando de Atabapo walked down to the dock, boarded their boat, and crossed the river to San Carlos and to Venezuela.

After dinner that night Londoño filled me in on what had happened since I left San Carlos.

"You know how it is in a small town," he said. "Most people sway with the wind, and when Cruxent and Vargas got to San Carlos all sorts of rumors about you were circulated. It was said that the night of the dance you asked every girl there to go to bed with you."

"That's the trouble," I said. "I didn't ask anybody."

"Another thing," said Londoño; "those pictures you showed us of Africa. Some people said that your only purpose in traveling was to take pictures of nude women. One rumor had it that you have a machine which allows you to see diamonds under the ocean, and others insisted that you have a secret map from the United States Government which shows uranium deposits in the Upper Orinoco and that that was the purpose of your trip.

270

"You were also accused of bribing Don Manuel and Perales so that they would allow you to get into Venezuela. And, of course, they said you were a drunkard, but some people say that about everybody.

"But I hardly drink at all," I said, "and I didn't bribe anybody."

"Look, Hector," said Londoño, "you don't have to tell me. I know, and so do most of the people in San Carlos.

"Another thing, nobody likes either Vargas or Cruxent. Vargas seemed to think he was in charge here after Don Manuel left, and he'd get drunk and give orders which nobody carried out.

"And as for Cruxent, most people laugh at him. Every morning he comes out of his house and takes exercises dressed in shorts, high white boots, and a T-shirt which says, 'Yardley University,' on it."

"Never heard of it," I said. "Yardley's the name of an after-shave lotion."

I had planned to cross to San Carlos at ten the next morning to demand a written explanation from Cruxent as to why I was called back, but I was too late. I was awakened at eight by the sound of an outboard motor, and when I ran to the window I saw two men sitting in the stern of a boat that was going upriver toward Atabapo.

One was Vargas, the other Cruxent, wearing a clean white T-shirt which snugly fit his firmly muscled torso. Across its front were the words, "Yale University."

For the first time in more than a week I laughed uproariously.

Well, that's about all there is to say about my expedition to discover the headwaters of the Orinoco. I did go across to San Carlos, but Don Manuel did not know or would not say any more about why I was called back. All he would do was confirm what

I already knew, that he could not give me permission to try again.

I spent the rest of ten quiet days in San Felipe, waiting for the *Aida* Catalina to arrive to fly Severo, Teolo, and me back to Bogotá.

During that time I wrote a lengthy explanation of what had happened to the Colombian foreign office requesting it to ask the Venezuelan Government why I was turned back so near to the end of my lengthy journey.

As this is written, nearly two years later, no reply has been received from Caracas.

Of course, I know the answer. It appeared in Bogotá's newspaper *El Tiempo* only a few weeks after my return. The dispatch said:

14 EXPLORERS GOING TO THE UPPER ORINOCO
TO MAKE INVESTIGATION
Caracas, April 15. (UP)—Fourteen men will ascend in May the Upper Orinoco to penetrate the areas of the Sierra Parima looking for new scientific experiences. The expedition consists of ten Venezuelan and four French scientists, whose investigations are sponsored by the government.

The French scientists are: Professor J. M. Cruxent, the Geologist Marc de Ciurieux and the Professors José Grelier and Léon Croizat, belonging to the named group "Luis de Liotard," famous for its numerous experiences in these kinds of investigations.

And on December 10 the New York *Times* reported that the American Geographical Society had received the following cable:

Greetings from the headwaters of the Orinoco River.

The cable was signed by Doctor José M. Cruxent.

An Epilogue

It was Friday afternoon, and I had only a little more than twenty-four hours in Rio de Janeiro. I was in one of those fashionable shops on the Avenida Rio Branco, which is surely the most beautiful thoroughfare in all the world, not excluding the Champs Élysées.

The shop was small, and in the window there was nothing except a suède coat and a few brightly colored scarves of the most modern design.

The coat was beautifully cut and of the best suède, but it was not worth the small fortune the elderly lady who ran the shop was asking for it. Nevertheless, I knew that after we had haggled over the price for a while I would buy the coat. I wanted it for Madeline.

I will never know why I glanced up at that particular moment. Instinct? Fate? Accident? I'm not sure, but I was examining the suède in the bright sunlight streaming in through the show window, when I looked up and saw Catani pass.

She was older, of course, and she was wearing a simple white dress which contrasted exquisitely with her dark skin. Her hair was cut short and was worn straight; she had on a tiny white hint of a hat, and her only make-up was a slash of pale red on her mouth. She was still beautiful.

I dropped the coat on the counter and ran to the street, shouting.

"Catani," I shouted, and again, "Catani."

On one side of her was a short, middle-aged woman who was also dressed in white, in what was obviously a nurse's uniform. Between them they were holding the hands of a small boy in a blue sailor suit; he was probably three years old, and when

Catani, the nurse, and he turned to look at me I could see that the child was her son.

"Catani," I repeated for the third time, running up to her.

For just a second her eyes widened with fear, and the color drained from her face. Then she regained her composure.

"Yes?" she asked.

"Catani," I said, "don't you remember me?"

She looked at the nurse, then smiled, rather condescendingly.

"There must," she said, "be some mistake. You have, perhaps, confused me with someone else."

The little boy began to whimper, and the nurse lifted him into her arms.

"My name," said Catani, "is——" And she mentioned the name.

"Oh," I said, backing away. "Of course. I'm terribly sorry. I can see now that I have confused you with a girl I once knew. I apologize."

She smiled graciously, affectionately patted the boy on the head, and continued down the wide boulevard, walking, as I once read great actresses should walk, as if a gentle wind was blowing at the small of her back.

She did not look back. In her entire life Catani has never looked back—only ahead.

During the next few months I invented a good many stories about Catani. Some of them were bitter and some amusing, some rather dull, a few filled with imaginative detail, but none half so interesting as what had really happened.

Late one afternoon about six months later, just as I was about to go home from the office, the phone rang, and when I answered it a soft, cultured voice said, "This is Señor da Silva, as you may remember."

"Of course," I said. "I'm delighted to hear your voice again. Where are you?"

"Right here in Bogotá," he said. "I shall be here only for tonight, on a business deal, and I thought we might be able to have a drink someplace."

I invited Da Silva to the house for dinner, and he accepted. When I picked him up at the hotel, I was shocked at his appearance. He was now a very old man. He was no longer fat, and the folds of yellow skin hung loosely from his face and body; his tiny blue eyes had faded in color and were deep-sunken, huge, dark circles underneath, and the sideburns, which were all that remained of his hair, were almost completely white. Although the diamonds were gone, he still wore the huge gold chain across his once-enormous belly. His suit was newly pressed, magnificently cut, and of the best linen, but it was an old suit, and there was a tiny ill-made patch on the jacket.

He smiled at me through his discolored teeth, his eyes lighting up behind the thick lenses of the rimless glasses, and he gave me a cold, blue-veined hand.

"It is good to see you, Señor Acebes," he said. "I have remembered our meeting on the boat and our talk later in Manáos with great pleasure."

I felt sure that he was telling the truth and that, as nearly as he was able, he was probably fond of me.

At dinner Señor da Silva did most of the talking, and, as always, talked beautifully and had something to say. He had, within the last year, he said, been back to Paris, and he compared the gray, defeated city he had seen with the carefree capital he remembered from his youth.

"Of course," I remember his saying once, "it may be that Paris has not changed at all. It may only be that I have changed.

"I am now too old for romance, and that is almost the sole reason for visiting Paris."

Madeline was fascinated with him, and I, naturally, did not even consider asking him about Catani until we had finished eating. While we were having brandy and coffee in my den he suddenly stopped whatever it was he was discussing at the moment and grinned at me like a mischievous small boy.

"You are," he said, "a remarkable man, Señor Acebes. Here it is two hours since you picked me up at my hotel, and you have not yet mentioned Catani, although it is obvious that nothing else has been on your mind.

"I am not sure that at your age I would have been so patient."

Then he told me the story. I am repeating it here mainly in my own words because that is easier and because there are a few details I must alter slightly, as Da Silva did not.

After I left Manáos, Da Silva said, he was ill for several weeks, confined to his bed in the hotel room. Naturally Catani was bored, but she was kind to him, and it was only on his insistence that she went for a walk every afternoon.

She was almost never gone for much more than an hour, but one day she did not return until considerably after dark, and, when she did, Da Silva could tell that something was wrong. She looked pale and nervous and, when he spoke to her, did not seem to hear what he was saying.

She apologized for being late, ordered supper for him, and, shortly after he had eaten, announced that she was tired and went to bed in the next room. Since Da Silva suffered from insomnia, he could tell from her breathing that she was not asleep. She did not actually doze off until just after sunup, and then slept for only a little more than an hour.

The next day she looked somewhat hollow-eyed but I remember Da Silva saying, "She could never seem less than magnificent to a man with eyes to see." She dressed carefully, and then said she had an errand to run. Just before she left, Da Silva said, "Is it another young man, Catani?" There had been two or three since I left Manáos. "None of them serious," said Da Silva, "just necessary. Young men were then as important to her as breathing."

She shook her head, but he knew she was lying, and when she returned that night at nearly midnight she told him what had happened.

Walking through one of the public gardens the afternoon before, she had met a young Brazilian Navy officer who was in Manáos on a minor diplomatic mission. He had stopped to speak to her, then had bought her a coffee, and by the time he returned her to the hotel he had hinted that he was in love with her.

There was nothing particularly unusual in that, except for the fact that Catani was also in love with him.

"I would have thought," said Da Silva, "that such an emotion was impossible for her, but I would have been wrong. Love like that cannot be pretended, and it is impossible to disguise it. She was like a small, happy child.

"When I asked her where the young officer was from, she said that he was from Rio de Janeiro.

" 'Well,' I said, 'there are no problems, then. You can go to Rio with him; he can establish you in an apartment, and you can be lovers.'

"She shook her head vigorously. 'No,' she said. 'I want to marry him.'

"I am," Da Silva went on, "an old man, and nothing much surprises me now, but I believe I must have gasped.

" 'But, Catani,' I said, 'that is impossible. You know——'

" 'Yes,' she said. 'I know what I am, but I wish to marry him, and he wishes to marry me.'

" 'Have you told him?' I asked.

"Catani shook her head a second time, and as she replied she did not look at me, 'I have told him many lies,' she said. 'I have said that you are my uncle, that I have lived much of my life in a convent in Portugal, and that you want to meet him. Will you?'

"I am not a man of nobility," said Da Silva, "and I did not myself wish to lose Catani, but I said that I would."

The young Navy officer came to the hotel room the next afternoon, and Da Silva could not have been more surprised. He was by no means handsome; his body was squat, and, although he was in his early twenties, he already had the beginnings of a paunch; his dark hair was beginning to thin, and there was a slight cast to one of his deep brown eyes.

However, he had a pleasant smile, and he was gentle and without guile, and he was deeply in love with Catani. His family was one of Brazil's oldest and most distinguished, but they were not particularly wealthy, and when Catani left the room the young officer, in an impulsive and altogether pleasant way, told Da Silva that although he was sure he would never be able to win his niece he was determined to try.

Da Silva grinned at him. " 'Of course,' he said, 'after the way my niece has been brought up, she is, naturally, expected to make a brilliant marriage, but you may have a chance with her.' "

The boy was delighted.

Well, there is not much more to the story.

A few days later, although he was still not quite recovered, Da Silva took his convent-educated niece to Rio, and the young officer met them at the boat. Catani, outfitted in a new and completely conservative wardrobe selected and paid for by Da Silva, met the family a few days later. They were delighted with her, and the wedding took place two months after that.

There was, said Da Silva, a good deal about it in the Brazilian newspapers.

"Are they happy?" I asked.

"Completely," he said.

"Did Catani ever tell her husband that she had lied to him?" I wanted to know.

Da Silva lifted his brandy glass and, after taking a sip, winked at me maliciously. "The night before her wedding," he said, "Catani came to me, weeping. She said that she could not go through with it, that she had to tell her husband-to-be the truth. Otherwise, she said, she would be unable to sleep at night.

"I solved the problem for her very simply. I asked her which she would rather do: be truthful and unmarried or untruthful and married.

"It took her almost no time at all to decide in favor of the latter, and that night she slept like a baby."

He placed his glass on the table.

"I am afraid," he said, "that all this will not please the moralists, but then life so seldom does. I have heard there is a second child on the way. Fortunately the first resembles his mother, and, if the second is a girl, Catani wishes her to be educated in a convent."

Then he grinned.

I did not want to ask him, but I had to know.

"Do you think she is faithful to her husband?" I asked.

"He is away a good deal of the time," said Da Silva, "but of her faithfulness to him I am certain. She is now a most moral woman, and she is also quite dull.

"By the way," he said a few minutes later, "you remember that expedition I mentioned to you?"

"You mean the search for diamonds?"

He nodded. "After you left Manáos," he said, "Catani met another young man. He was of a romantic spirit and also something of an adventurer.

"Like so many men before him, he immediately was taken with Catani and wished to have her as his mistress, but she only laughed at him.

"She did not much like him, and he was very poor.

"One day I suggested the expedition to the Upper Amazon to him, as I had to you, and he leapt at the chance. If he found the diamonds, he would be a very rich man, and he felt sure that Catani would be interested in him.

"He was most inexperienced, but with my help he finally got together enough men and enough money for the trip. Then he set off."

Da Silva paused, the tiny eyes gleaming with evil and, I guessed, amusement.

"How," I asked, "did he make out?"

"I cannot be sure," said Da Silva. "Neither he nor his men returned.

"As I have told you," he went on, "those Indians are extremely unfriendly, and I was not at the time prepared to give up Catani."

He half filled his glass again and added, "You know, Señor Acebes, it will take a great deal of money when those daughters of yours are prepared to marry. It costs a man a lot to provide a dowry, even for a niece."

The next morning Da Silva went back to Manáos, and that afternoon I realized I had forgotten to ask him a question. "Who did he think was the father of Catani's boy?"

I suppose that a book should have an ending, but this one cannot. By the time it appears I shall be in Central Africa on another expedition, and next year, or the year after, I plan to follow another trail into the Amazon Basin, this time into the wilderness where Colonel Fawcett disappeared while searching for El Dorado, the city whose streets were said to be paved with gold. I do not expect to find such a city, but I do hope to unravel some of the tangled legends about the colonel.

And there are other expeditions to come after that, many others. One of my business associates in Bogotá once asked me if I thought I would ever grow up.

When I asked him what he meant, he said, "Well, it's childish to be running off into some jungle every few months. What would happen if everybody did that?"

I shrugged. "I don't know," I said, "what would happen?"

He blustered, and he fumbled, and he looked at me as if I were out of my mind, but he did not answer my question.

No one ever has.

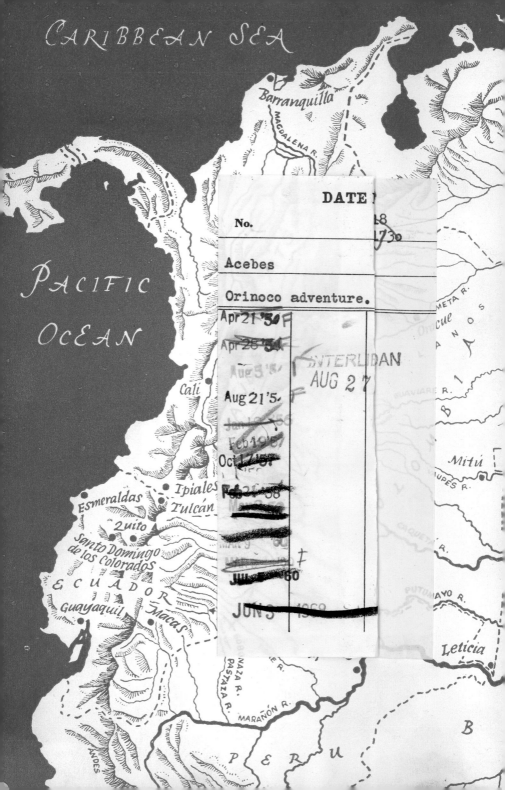

A Beginning-to-Read Book

It's Summer, Dear Dragon

by Margaret Hillert

Illustrated by David Schimmell

NORWOOD HOUSE PRESS

DEAR CAREGIVER,

The *Beginning-to-Read* series is a carefully written collection of classic readers you may remember from your own childhood. Each book features text comprised of common sight words to provide your child ample practice reading the words that appear most frequently in written text. The many additional details in the pictures enhance the story and offer the opportunity for you to help your child expand oral language and develop comprehension.

Begin by reading the story to your child, followed by letting him or her read familiar words and soon your child will be able to read the story independently. At each step of the way, be sure to praise your reader's efforts to build his or her confidence as an independent reader. Discuss the pictures and encourage your child to make connections between the story and his or her own life. At the end of the story, you will find reading activities and a word list that will help your child practice and strengthen beginning reading skills.

Above all, the most important part of the reading experience is to have fun and enjoy it!

Shannon Cannon

Shannon Cannon,
Literacy Consultant

Norwood House Press • P.O. Box 316598 • Chicago, Illinois 60631
For more information about Norwood House Press please visit our website at *www.norwoodhousepress.com* or call 866-565-2900.

LIBRARY OF CONGRESS CATALOGING-IN-PUBLICATION DATA
  Hillert, Margaret.
   It's summer, dear dragon / by Margaret Hillert ; illustrated by David Schimmell.
     p. cm. — (A beginning-to-read book)
   Summary: "A boy and his pet dragon enjoy a summer day by swimming, having a picnic, playing teeball, and seeing a fireworks show"—Provided by publisher.
   ISBN-13: 978-1-59953-313-1 (lib. ed. : alk. paper)
   ISBN-10: 1-59953-313-8 (lib. ed. : alk. paper) [1. Dragons--Fiction. 2. Summer--Fiction.] I. Schimmell, David, ill. II. Title. III. Title: It is summer, dear Dragon.
   PZ7.H558Itu 2009
   [E]--dc22
                                                2009003889

Manufactured in the United States of America.

Come here. Come here.
Come to my house.
I will do this and we can have fun.

Oh. Oh.
My mother wants me.
I will come back.

4

What, Mother?
Do you want me to help?
I can work, work, work.

Yes, yes.
Put all of this away.
Then you can go back there.

6

Get in. Get in.
Now we can play.
This is good.

7

I will put this on here.
Then we can eat.
It will be fun.

Here comes Father.

Come on.
Come on.
See what Mother did.
It looks good, good, good.

Oh, boy.
Do you see what I see?
Can we go now?

It looks so good!
Here is one for me—
and one for you.

Come now.
Put this on.
We have to go.

Yes.
I want to go.
I like to play.

Away we go.
Away, away, away.

Here we are.
This is the spot.
I see my friends.

Now I will do this.
One, two, three!
There it goes!

Did you see me, Father?
Did you see me?

Yes. Yes.
You were good.

Now we have to go.
We will go away, away, away.
We will see something good.

What was that?
Did you see that?

Look, look.
Oh, oh, oohhh!

Here you are with me.
And here I am with you.
What fun. What fun, dear dragon.

READING REINFORCEMENT

The following activities support the findings of the National Reading Panel that determined the most effective components for reading instruction are: Phonemic Awareness, Phonics, Vocabulary, Fluency, and Text Comprehension.

Phonemic Awareness: Syllabication

Oral Blending: Say the following words, clapping the syllables as you say them. Ask your child to tell you how many syllables are in each word:

spark-1	sparkle-2	pebble-2	little-2	lit-1
mother-2	fireworks-2	summer-2	play-1	playing-2
father-2	uniform-3	pool-1	splash-1	splashing-2
favorite-3	baseball-2	holiday-3		

Phonics: Consonant + le Syllabication

1. Write the following word parts on separate index cards: spar, sprin, bub, mar, pud, mid, wig, gig, bot, lit, puz, daz.

2. Write the following consonant + **le** syllables on separate index cards: kle, ble, dle, gle, tle, zle.

3. Help your child match the correct consonant + **le** syllable with the word parts to make complete words. Each word ending will be used more than once (answers: spar/kle, sprin/kle, bub/ble, mar/ble, pud/dle, mid/dle, wig/gle, gig/gle, bot/tle, lit/tle, puz/zle, daz/zle).

Vocabulary: Summer Senses

1. On a blank sheet of paper, make five columns by drawing four lines. Write the following words at the top of each column: see, hear, smell, taste, and touch. Ask your child to read the words aloud.

2. Ask your child to think of things people see, hear, smell, taste and touch in the summer. Write your child's responses in the correct column.

Examples:

<u>see</u>	<u>hear</u>	<u>smell</u>	<u>taste</u>	<u>touch</u>
sunshine	children playing	barbeque	ice cream	pool water
sprinklers	water splashing	grass	watermelon	grass
fireworks	crowds cheering	sunscreen	corn on the cob	baseball bat

3. Ask your child to write five sentences about summer—using one sense word from each column.

4. The following sentence starter may help your child:

In summer, I can (see, hear, smell, taste, touch) _____.

Fluency: Choral Reading

1. Reread the story with your child at least two more times while your child tracks the print by running a finger under the words as they are read. Ask your child to read the words he or she knows with you.

2. Reread the story aloud together. Be careful to read at a rate that your child can keep up with.

3. Repeat choral reading and allow your child to be the lead reader and ask him or her to change from a whisper to a loud voice while you follow along and change your voice.

Text Comprehension: Discussion Time

1. Ask your child to retell the sequence of events in the story.

2. To check comprehension, ask your child the following questions:
   - How did the boy help his mother?
   - What is the word that describes what we do when we eat outside? (picnic)
   - What holiday do you think they were celebrating when they saw the fireworks?
   - What do you like to do in summer? Why?

WORD LIST

***It's Summer, Dear Dragon* uses the 65 words listed below.**
This list can be used to practice reading the words that appear in the text.
You may wish to write the words on index cards and use them to help your
child build automatic word recognition. Regular practice with these words
will enhance your child's fluency in reading connected text.

all	eat	in	play	was
am		is	put	we
and	Father	it		were
are	for		see	what
away	friends	like	so	will
	fun	look(s)	something	with
back			spot	work
be	get	me		
boy	go		that	yes
	goes	Mother	the	you
can		my	then	
come(s)	good		there	
		now	this	
	have			
dear	help	of	three	
did	here	oh	to	
do	house	on	two	
dragon		one		
	I		want(s)	

ABOUT THE AUTHOR Margaret Hillert has written over 80 books for
children who are just learning to read. Her books
have been translated into many different languages and over a million children
throughout the world have read her books. She first started writing poetry as
a child and has continued to write for children and adults throughout her life. A
first grade teacher for 34 years, Margaret is now retired from teaching and lives in
Michigan where she likes to write, take walks in the morning, and care for her three cats.

Photograph by Glenna Washburn

ABOUT THE ADVISER Shannon Cannon contributed the activities pages that appear in
this book. Shannon serves as a literacy consultant and provides
staff development to help improve reading instruction. She is a frequent presenter at educational
conferences and workshops. Prior to this she worked as an elementary school teacher and as
president of a curriculum publishing company.